CALLE
SPIRIT UAL
MATURITY

A Study of Hebrews, Chapters 1-4

by Eva Gibson

Discovering the Heart of God Series

A Bible Study

AGLOW® INTERNATIONAL
P.O. Box 1548
Lynnwood, WA 98046-1548
USA

Cover design by Paz Design Group

Aglow International is an interdenominational organization of Christian women. Our mission is to lead women to Jesus Christ and provide opportunity for Christian women to grow in their faith and minister to others.

Our publications are used to help women find a personal relationship with Jesus Christ, to enhance growth in their Christian experience, and to help them recognize their roles and relationship according to Scripture.

For more information about our organization, please write to Aglow International, P.O. Box 1548, Lynnwood, WA 98046-1548, USA, call (206) 775-7282, or FAX (206) 778-9615.

Unless otherwise noted all Scripture quotations are from the New King James Version (NKJV). Copyright ©1979, 1980, 1982, Thomas Nelson, Inc. Other versions are abbreviated as follows: New American Standard Bible (NASB), New International Version (NIV), The Amplified Bible (TAB), and The Living Bible (TLB).

ISBN 1-56616-007-3

2 3 4 5 Printing/Year 96 95

AGLOW BIBLE STUDIES

<u>Basic Series</u>

God's Daughter
Practical Aspects of a Christian Woman's Life

The Holy Spirit and His Gifts
A Study of the Scriptural Gifts

Coming Alive in the Spirit
The Spirit-Led Life

<u>Discovering the Heart of God Series</u>

Called to Spiritual Maturity
A Study of Hebrews, Chapters 1-4

Getting to Know the Heart of God
A Study of Hebrews, Chapters 5-10

Practicing Truth in the Family of God
A Study of Hebrews, Chapters 11-13

Write or FAX for a free catalog

For important information on how to order a
Leader's Guide *for all three Bible studies of Hebrews*
by Eva Gibson, please see next page.

How to Order a *Leader's Guide*

We have just made the ordering process for a Bible study *Leader's Guide* as easy as dialing the phone! The Aglow order number, 1-800-755-2456, puts you right through to us.

Now you will be able to order one or more *Leader's Guides* at the same time you order from our warehouse and you will be billed $1. for each *Leader's Guide* on your Aglow invoice. We encourage you to order *Leader's Guides* at the same time you order other Aglow materials to save additional charges.

In memory of my dearest friend,
Geri Mitch

Dedicated to Sharon Leach
Lover of God
Student of His Word
My special friend

Contents

Contents

Introduction

"Grow up spiritually? Of course I want to! But how do I do it?"

Probably most of us, if we're honest, feel a faint discontent at our level of spiritual maturity. Oh, it isn't that we don't read our Bibles or have fellowship with other Christians. It's just that so many things demand our attention.

It's also possible to settle into a ho-hum sort of existence. *Sure I'd like to pray more and understand the deep things in God's Word. But, well, things are going along okay for me right now.* . . . Except. . . . Except. . . .

It's not really okay. There's a longing inside for more.

Or it could be that life is stretching you to the limit right now. Confusion, helplessness, a "where do I go now?" can try the sturdiest individual. It's difficult then to understand why hard things happen to people who love God and want to serve Him.

Sometimes, if we're honest, we have to admit that growing up doesn't hold a lot of appeal. Grownups have to work long hours and do things they'd rather not do. Sometimes it means keeping on doing the right thing when we'd much rather do the wrong thing.

No, it's not easy to grow into mature Christians. It takes sacrifice and determination and plain hard work. Sometimes it almost seems it would be easier to simply quit.

It wasn't easy for the Hebrew Christians to grow up either. Persecution was rising and some of them were barely hanging onto their faith. Still others were retreating.

Then a letter began to circulate. Although we're not sure of the author—or even who exactly the readers were—one thing we do know; the Hebrew Christians to whom this book was addressed were just like you and me.

The letter was a call to maturity. An exhortation to go on, no matter what. Charles Swindoll describes it as "a song of encouragement with a few resonate notes of warning, calling them back to the Way, the Truth, and the Life."[1]

The encouragement needed by those long-ago Hebrews is the same kind of encouragement today's woman needs to keep going on, no matter what happens. We need to be reminded to fix our attention on Jesus Christ. To grow in spiritual maturity, even when it hurts.

The only way to grow up is to persevere.

The art of persevering is only perfected as we look to Jesus, the Author and Perfector of our faith.

How to Use This Book:

This study is designed to help you grow in spiritual maturity. Each study is in four parts:

1. *God Speaks* is an inductive study.

2. *I Listen* has suggestions adapted to journaling to help you apply the truth you're learning to specific areas in your life.

3. *We Talk Together* contains encouragement and suggestions for prayer.

4. *Walking Along Together* shows how God made each week's scripture passage real to the author.

The study is designed to be done a little each day, five days a week. You will profit most if you take the time daily to ask the Holy Spirit to

---

1. Charles R. Swindoll, *The Preeminent Person of Christ, A Study in Hebrews 1-10* (Fullerton, CA: Insight for Living, 1989), p. 3.

be your teacher before you begin.

Use each day's study questions to work through the scripture passage. They will prepare you to make daily application in the *I Listen* and help you present your praise and prayers to God in *We Talk Together* with deepened insight. The narrative section is to be read at the end of the week after you have completed all five sections.

You will need this study guide, the NKJV translation, a notebook, and/or your journal, dictionary, and concordance.

It would also be good to have a commentary, Bible dictionary, and several Bible translations.

If you're part of a group, you'll find it most helpful to complete the study questions before you meet. Solidify what you're learning by being ready to share what you've learned and how it applies to your life. Write down any unanswered questions you may have. Your leader or others in the group may be able to help you further.

For Leaders, a Guide

The book of Hebrews is written to women whom God wants to draw into a deeper relationship with Himself. Women who have problems, women who want more but who aren't quite sure what it is they're looking for. Women who want to grow in spiritual maturity.

Although Hebrews is difficult to understand, it is also filled with some of the richest teaching about our Lord Jesus Christ. (See page 4 if you wish to write for a Leader's Guide on this study.)

You've taken a giant first step in Christian maturity by choosing to study it.

1

• • •

Called to Listen to the Son

Hebrews 1:1-4

❦ DAY 1 ❦

GOD SPEAKS

THE PROLOGUE

Read **Hebrews 1:1-4**.

1. When your best friend introduces you to someone, what does she say? How does she describe you? What does her introduction reveal about your relationship?

____

____

2. In a majestic, stirring paragraph, the writer of Hebrews introduces us immediately to the glory and greatness of God's Son, the Lord Jesus Christ. What does this tell you about God? About Jesus Christ? About the writer of this book? About the readers?

Speaking thro his son-
authority and heir. They
made the universe. God
Sustains the world thro
his word. Redemption
in Jesus.

Read verse 1 in as many different translations as possible. For example *The Amplified Bible* says, "In many separate revelations—each of which set forth a portion of the Truth—and in different ways God spoke of old to [our] forefathers in and by the prophets."

3. What insights did you gain from reading the different translations?

Through the prophets -
at various times and
in various ways

This verse helps us understand something about the original Hebrew Christians the letter was addressed to. The Jews knew about prophets. When prophets spoke, the people listened. (When they didn't listen, afterwards they always wished they had.)

The prophets were God's mouthpieces. They were responsible to speak God's message without additives or explanations.

Read **2 Peter 2:1, 21**.

4. What does Peter say about "false prophets and false teachers"?

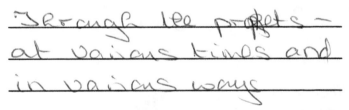

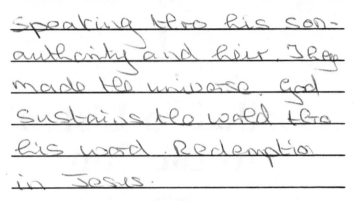

Introduce heresy
disclaiming the sovereignty of
God

A footnote in the NIV Study Bible on Hebrews 1:1 gives further understanding:

(v. 1), *"through the prophets.* All OT writers are here viewed as [prophets] in that their testimony was preparation for the coming of Christ; cf. 'by his son' (v. 2), a new and unique category of revelation in contrast to that of the prophets, *at many times and in various ways.* The OT revelation was fragmentary and occasional, lacking fullness and finality."

5. Read the following examples of God speaking and write down the means He used.

   Isaiah 6:1-4: Vision

   Genesis 28:11-18: Dream

   Judges 13:2-21: Angel

   Jeremiah 18:1-4: Everyday life situations making pottery

6. Now answer these questions about Hebrews 1:1.

   a. How did God's prophets speak? Various ways

   b. When did they speak? " times

   c. What are some of the things they said? Instruction / direction what would happen.

I LISTEN (Journaling Suggestion)

What do you most want to communicate about Jesus to another person? Write a sentence or two about Jesus to introduce that person to Jesus. How did writing it make you feel?

WE TALK TOGETHER (Prayer)

Memory experts tell us that one of the best ways to remember the name of a person we've just been introduced to is to use her name in direct address back to her.

God has introduced us to His Son. In your notebook, acknowledge His presence in your life by writing a sentence or two directly to Him.

Allow Him to speak directly to your heart. Respond from your heart to His. Include a truth from today's study that will help you apply what you're learning to your life. Finish this prayer in your own words:

"Son of God, the prophets have been your mouthpieces in the past. But now it is You through whom God speaks. Lord Jesus, help me to listen as I . . .

DAY 2

GOD SPEAKS

GOD SPEAKS THROUGH HIS SON

Read **Hebrews 1:1-2**.

1. The many ways someone speaks about another person is important. What would you say about your best friend in a letter to another friend? What would you say about her face to face to another person?

   ____

   ____

   ____

   ____

2. Anytime we do a Bible study we need to ask two questions:
   a. What is the author saying?
   b. What is he saying about it?
   Address these two questions to Hebrews 1:1-2. Write down your answers.

How God spoke in the past
and is speaking now.

3. The thought introduced in verse one continues in the first part of verse two. Other thought-provoking questions to ask and answer:
   a. How and when does God speak through His Son?

   ____

   ____

   b. How is the message of the prophets different from that of the Son?

   ____

   ____

Read **Galatians 4:4.**

4. What does the writer of Hebrews mean by "these last days"?

____

Read **John 1:1-17.**

5. How do these verses give additional insight to Hebrews 1:1-2?

____

6. What title does John give Jesus in these verses?

____

Thought to carry into your day: The prophets were mouthpieces of God's Word. God's Son *is* the Word of God.

God's message for me today is spoken through God's Son, the Lord Jesus Christ. When the Son speaks, God speaks.

Called to Maturity

I LISTEN

What does it mean to you to be living in an age when God speaks through a Person, His Son, the Lord Jesus Christ? Try to put your feelings into words you could share with another person.

WE TALK TOGETHER

John called Jesus *the Word of God* in John 1:1. Complete this prayer: "Word of God, I praise You for making Yourself known to me through the words You spoke when You were here on earth. I'm thankful that over the centuries Your Word . . ."

❦ DAY 3 ❦

GOD SPEAKS

WHAT DOES GOD SAY ABOUT JESUS?

Read **Hebrews 1:1-4**.

1. Jot down seven facts that describe your best friend. Why did you choose these particular facts?

____

____

____

____

2. Jot down seven facts describing Jesus Christ from verses 2 and 3. Why do you think the writer chose these particular ones?

1. Heir of all things. 2 made universe. 3 Radiance. 4 Exact representation 5. Sustains universe. 6. Purification of sin. 7 sitting at in heaven

The writer's purpose in writing this letter is to magnify the significance of Jesus and to encourage his readers to look to Him. Our natural tendency when hard times come is to look at circumstances, people, at our own selves. It's easy then to lose heart and give up.

3. How would these facts in these verses best encourage the readers to look to Jesus?

His authority and power as Son of God.

4. Are you facing hard times right now? Write about it in a short paragraph. Reread the description of Jesus Christ. How can these facts encourage you to keep on? Write about that in still another paragraph.

I LISTEN

What fact do you hear repeated most often when people introduce you to others? Why do you think that particular one is most often mentioned?

In your Bible study you were asked which fact/phrase about Jesus Christ pulled most strongly at your heart. Write it down in your journal. Respond to it in your own words.

WE TALK TOGETHER

Put one fact from the description of Jesus Christ into a prayer, e.g., "Heir of all things, I love You. Because you're heir of all, I put everything I have and am into your hands. I give you . . ."

❦ DAY 4 ❦

GOD SPEAKS

MORE ABOUT JESUS FROM OTHER VERSES

Read **Hebrews 1:2-3.**

1. Write the following seven phrases describing Jesus in your notebook. Use the verses that follow to add to your understanding of who Jesus is, then write a sentence or two about each phrase.
   Appointed heir of all things. (Rom. 8:17)
   Through whom also He made the universe. (John 1:3; Col. 1:16)
   Brightness of His glory. (Mal 4:2; Luke 1:78-79; John 1:14, 18; Rev. 1:12-16)
   Express image of His person. (John 14:9; Col. 1:15)
   Upholding all things. (Col. 1:17 NIV)
   Purged our sins. (Heb. 9:26)
   Sat down at the right hand of the Majesty on high. (Heb. 1:13, 8:1, 10:12, 12:2; Col. 3:1; 1 Pet. 3:22)

2. What other verses came to your mind as you studied? Add them to the above list.

   ____

   ____

3. Think about how you are better able to function in the following situations because of what you've learned today about who Jesus is.
   - Your best friend tells you she questions whether or not God is really in control because of all the awful things that happen in the world.
   - A cultist comes to your door and tries to tell you that Jesus isn't really God.

- Your teenager runs away from home and you don't know where he is.

I LISTEN

It's easiest to understand what someone is saying about someone else when we understand the meaning of key words. Look up these words from verses 2-3 in your dictionary: *heir, exact, image, glory,* and *purge*. Try to simplify the definitions in your own words, then rewrite the verses in a simplified paraphrase that expresses your own attitude toward the Lord.

WE TALK TOGETHER

The one truth that stood out to me most boldly today about Jesus is . . . e.g., "Upholder of all things, Your power holds all things together. Because it does, I can trust you to hold me together, today, even as I . . .

DAY 5

GOD SPEAKS

JESUS COMPARED TO THE ANGELS

Read **Hebrews 1:1-4**.

1. What do you think about angels? What would you say if you had the opportunity to introduce one? How would you describe their particular ministry in your life? In the lives of your friends?

____

____

____

____

____

____

Called to Maturity

Verse 4 is part of the prologue introducing Jesus Christ. It also introduces the majestic discourse that follows in verses 5-14 on Christ's superiority to the angels. This is important because most Jews considered the angels to be exalted beings since they were involved in giving the law at Mt. Sinai. Read about it in Acts 7:38, 53; Galatians 3:19.

2. The name Jesus inherited is "so much better than the angels." What additional insight does knowing Christ's superiority to angels give you?

____

____

3. Using a concordance, find another reference to Christ where the writer of Hebrews uses the word *excellent*. What would you say the author is trying to emphasize to his readers about Jesus Christ?

____

____

4. Summing up:
   a. Many Bible scholars consider Hebrews 1:1-4 a prologue. One definition of prologue is "a preliminary act or course of action foreshadowing greater events." How does this thought heighten your sense of anticipation as you continue your study in Hebrews? Based on your study thus far, what can you hope to discover as you read?

   ____

   ____

   ____

   ____

b. Verses 1-4 introduce Jesus Christ in unforgettable terms. They also carry an implied command: Jesus is God's great Son, His final Word. Listen to Him. What are some of the ways you listen to Jesus?

____

____

c. Read Hebrews 12:25-27. How do these verses enhance Hebrews 1:1-4. What additional insight do they give about listening to God?

____

____

Challenge activity: Use your study Bible or Bible encyclopedia to research the background of the book of Hebrews.

I LISTEN

Has God spoken to your heart through His description of His Son? How can these verses imprint your life? Help you to persevere, even through hard times? Choose one of the phrases describing Jesus and incorporate it into a praise and/or prayer song addressed to Him. Allow your song to communicate the awe and majesty you've glimpsed this week about the diety of Jesus Christ. Allow it to express your need for His power to help you persevere until the end. To help you grow into spiritual maturity.

WE TALK TOGETHER

Jesus' name is superior to any other name. "Jesus Christ, Name above all Names, I worship You. I . . ."

WALKING ALONG TOGETHER

There's something special about spending time in the presence of our Lord. And when we think of His incomparable beauty and majesty, we want to linger even longer.

I caught a tiny glimpse of who He is when I was five years old. I remember going to my mother and telling her that I'd made up a poem. The words I recited to her expressed the longings caught inside my heart:

Jesus and I were walking along together;
We came to a tree and sat down together
And talked about what was up in heaven.

My mother was delighted with my first poetic attempt. She talked about it to anyone who would listen.

But the greatest delight for me was thinking about Jesus and me sitting together, talking, under *our* tree. Somehow I knew it was an apple tree.

Enjoying Jesus

Now that I'm grown I sometimes think back to that moment of insight. As young as I was, I was enjoying who Jesus is. I was lingering in His presence, allowing Him to touch the deep places in my heart.

In a way this simple act of focusing on Jesus, of listening and worshiping in His presence, was probably my first step toward spiritual maturity. Of course, I was limited in what I could understand. (I couldn't read yet.)

I had so much to learn. But little by little, here a little, there a little, I began to put together bits and pieces of information.

In times past God sometimes spoke face to face with His people. He spoke through the prophets. He spoke through dreams . . . He even spoke through object lessons and unusual happenings, such as famines.

But each of these was only a fragment, a tiny part of the whole revelation of what God wanted to reveal to the world.

It's a little like the fragments of information I received as I was growing up—each fragment was communicated in a different way.

Ways of Communicating

My dad was a silent man but occasionally he communicated important things when we were alone together. He'd show me beauty in the growth rings of a sawed off tree, single out a wild flower and tell me its name. Once he spanked me when I angrily rebelled against him.

Sometimes when I hurt myself my mother communicated with

words of comfort. Other times she put comfort into actions; her arms around me as she kissed the "owie" always made me feel better.

My teachers taught me how to read and do long division. One of them even gave me a set of encyclopedias that I read from cover to cover. I learned about crocodiles and Gulliver's travels and terrible diseases, such as smallpox and scarlet fever.

More Memories

A neighbor sent me a box of *National Geographic* magazines that I kept under my bed. Lying on my bed in the middle of summer, I'd canoe down a river into the heart of Africa or dig up an archeological ruin in far away Egypt.

All these things gave me information I could use and enjoy as I grew toward maturity. But none of these was complete in itself. I needed more . . . I still do . . .

God . . . has in these last days spoken to us by His Son. . . .

There's something glorious about the Word of God. Something wonderful and complete. And when God's Word comes through a Personality. . .

I'm older now. I can read His Word and in the first chapter of Hebrews God speaks to me through this glorious description of His Son, my Lord and Savior Jesus Christ.

My journal is beside me. I reach for it, copy the first descriptive phrase about Jesus. Directly underneath I write my response inside parentheses.

Appointed heir of all things

(Lord, being heir means you're in charge of everything. That's a glorious thought. Why do I so often think that circumstances and people are out of Your control?)

Through whom He made the universe

(God and Jesus standing together, speaking the world into existence. What creativity. What power! It's beyond my comprehension.)

Brightness of His glory

(The out-raying of God's glory. I can only imagine a little bit of what it must be like to be touched by that glory light.)

God Is Impressed on Jesus

Express image of His person

(I remember reading that *express image* means "exact reproduction." In the same way a stamp is impressed on coins and seals by an engraver, so is God's personality impressed on Jesus. Everything God is, is imprinted on Him. Jesus is God.)

Upholding all things

(All things that move and have their being. Even me as I rush from one responsibility to another!)

Purged our sins

(These words stop me dead in my tracks. Sins. The sins of the world. My sin. But Your blood removes the guilt and penalty. You cleanse me daily from my defilement.)

Sat down at the right hand of the Majesty on high

(Seated in Heaven. Your work completed. Finished. Because it is, I bow before You.)

The poem I wrote about Jesus when I'd only just begun reflected where I was as a small child. I'm writing another poem today, a grown-up version that will be different from my long ago one because I've grown in my understanding of Who God is. It will flow out of what He's teaching me in His Word about Himself.

In my new poem, Jesus and I will still walk together. We'll rest beneath a tree and talk about what's up in heaven. But this time I know He's sitting at God's right hand in heaven in a position of power. I recognize His sovereignty, His Oneness with His Father.

Jesus is my God. He's in charge. Powerful. Because He is, I can submit to Him.

My childhood poem and my grown-up one are different. Yet both of them are precious because each, in its own way, is a result of His sharing His heart with me.

We love each other.

He's beside me, helping me grow up.

2

• • •

Jesus, Greater Than the Angels

Hebrews 1:5-14

❦ DAY 1 ❦

GOD SPEAKS

JESUS, SUPERIOR TO ANGELS

Read **Hebrews 1:4-13.**

1. What were your childhood impressions of angels? What did you imagine angels looked like? How did they dress? What did they do?

____

____

Called to Maturity

2. These verses refer to angels ______ times. Write down each reference and one thing you observe about Jesus' superiority to angels.

   ____

   ____

   ____

3. One of the techniques the writer uses to prove Jesus is superior to angels is that of contrast. In these verses Christ is declared to be superior because He has inherited a ______________ superior to theirs. He is God's Son, and all the angels ______________ ______________. His angels are ______________ while Christ is Sovereign forever on the throne.

4. Observe the rhetorical questions (rhetorical questions are used to introduce a topic and/or emphasize a point). What is the writer emphasizing with each of these questions?

   ____

   ____

   ____

   ____

5. It is fascinating that most of the Old Testament quotations in this chapter are from the Psalms (Psalm 2:7 and 2 Samuel 7:14 in verse 5; Psalm 104:4 in verse 7; Psalm 45:6-7 in verses 8-9; Psalm 102:25-27 in verses 10-12; and Psalm 110:1 in verse 13). What does this tell you about the writer?

   ____

   ____

About the people he was writing to?

____

____

Last week we talked about two questions that we need to ask whenever we study a particular portion of Scripture:

a. What is the author saying?

b. What is he saying about it?

6. Ask these questions now about Hebrews 1:4-14. Condense your thoughts into one or two sentences for each question.

____

____

____

____

____

____

I LISTEN (Journaling Suggestion)

One thing we learn about the writer of Hebrews is that he loved the Psalms. We could probably use "Angels and Psalms" as a subtitle for this passage and be on track. Somehow the association of the Psalms with songs and angels with music has power to draw us to worship.

This week you'll be encouraged to read some of these quotations from the Psalms as part of your journaling experience. They will help you better understand the heart of God. They will draw you to worship Jesus Christ, the Son of God, the Creator of the world, the supreme King and Ruler of the earth.

The first Psalm reference is Psalm 2:7. God is speaking about Jesus Christ, His Son. What do these verses show you about the Father/Son relationship? About Jesus' power? His inheritance? How does it make you feel to realize that you can enter into this relationship by simply becoming God's child?

Also read verses 8-12. Put into your own words this picture of Jesus' glory and power.

WE TALK TOGETHER (Prayer)

Paraphrase Psalm 2:11-12 into a prayer of worship, e.g., "Lord Jesus, I revere Your name. I rejoice that I'm your child, but I tremble too. You are so great, so holy. How blessed I am to be able to take refuge in You!

DAY 2

GOD SPEAKS

GOD'S FIRSTBORN SON, WORTHY OF WORSHIP

Read **Hebrews 1:5-6**.

1. Describe a meaningful relationship you have observed between a father and a son. How does thinking about it now help you better understand Jesus' relationship with His Father? How does seeing Jesus and the Father in a close relationship enhance your own relationship with God (John 17:11)? How does it make you feel to know that, because of Jesus, you too, can call God, "Holy Father"?

A footnote from the *NIV Study Bible* tells us that the name suggests both remoteness and nearness; God is both awe-inspiring and loving.

In the prologue the author draws our attention to the excellence of Jesus Christ. Now he dwells on it in greater detail. To the Jews, a name stood for the character of a person, all he was and all he did. Jesus' name was *Son*.

2. What two ideas in verse 5 show that the name, *Son*, is a unique name belonging only to Jesus?

____

____

3. How does the name, *Son of God*, reveal Jesus' divine character, His oneness with the Father?

____

____

Psalm 2:7 is quoted in Acts 13:33 as fulfilled in Christ's resurrection.

Read **Psalm 2:7, Acts 13:32-37,** and **Romans 1:4-7.**

4. How does the resurrection prove Jesus is God's Son?

____

____

The author takes us from the resurrection, back to the birth of the Son into the world. There is beauty in verse 6. "When He again brings the firstborn into the world, He says, 'Let all the angels of God worship him.' "

5. Write a word picture of this glorious worship event (Luke 2:8-14) in a field in Bethlehem. Who was present? What did the shepherds see? What did the angel say? What did the heavenly host

proclaim? You might even want to put what you feel into a song.

____

____

____

____

____

I LISTEN

Have you ever been in a worship service where you felt God's glory? Did you sense the presence of holy angels? What did it mean to you to worship Jesus Christ? To worship God the Father? What do you think worship means to Jesus? To the Father? Write your thoughts in your journal.

WE TALK TOGETHER

If you are a child of God, you can address a prayer of praise and adoration to God as your Holy Father. Do it now. If you're not sure you're His child, write a prayer paraphrasing these verses: John 1:12, 3:16; Romans 3:23, 5:8 in your own words, asking Him to make you part of His family.

DAY 3

GOD SPEAKS

THE EXALTED KING

Read **Hebrews 1:7-9.**

1. In contrast to the angels' worship of the Son, the angels are next described as ministers. Many versions of the Bible translate this word as "servants." When you think of a servant, what comes to your mind? Do servants and angels connect in your thinking? If not, why not? If they do fit together, can you explain why?

2. In verse 7, the writer says angels are like flames of fire. How does this verse affirm Christ's power as revealed in verse 2?

3. The phrase, "But to the Son He says," connects the angels as servants to Christ as King. Write down five observations in verses 8-9.

4. Which of these observations is most meaningful to you right now?

One way we can better understand a particular scripture passage is to ask questions about it, then try to answer those that seem most important. We can sometimes find an answer by a closer observation of the context. Other times we will need to study other references in a concordance or by cross references in a study Bible. You may even want to seek help in a commentary or Bible dictionary. However, you will learn more if you do your own research in the Bible itself before going to secondary resources.

Sample questions:

a. What is a scepter of righteousness?
b. Who are the companions in verse 9?
c. What is the oil of gladness?

5. Write down two of your own questions. Try to answer one of them.

d. ____

e. ____

____

I LISTEN

There are many things in Psalm 45 that are hard to understand. But as we compare Hebrews 1:8-9 with Psalm 45:6-7, we can know that these verses describe our Lord Jesus, the Messiah, God's anointed Son. Write Psalm 45:6 in your journal. Underneath, write your own personal response in parentheses. Do the same with verse 7.

WE TALK TOGETHER

What truth about Jesus in these passages in Hebrews and Psalms touches you most deeply? Write a song of praise addressed to Son of God, Creator, or Exalted King.

❦ DAY 4 ❦

GOD SPEAKS

JESUS IS CREATOR GOD

Read **Hebrews 1:10-12.**

1. How does it make you feel to recognize that Christ was there in the beginning as God's agent in creation? That He laid the earth's foundation? Constructed heaven? How does it make you feel to know that the One who created it will outlast His creation?

____

____

____

2. The Hebrew Christians were facing rejection and persecution. How would the power displayed by Jesus Christ in creation be an encouragment to them?

____

____

3. The writer uses a word picture of God folding up the universe like a piece of worn out clothing. In what way does this metaphor contrast the creation to Jesus?

____

____

4. How can this picture of Jesus Christ give you hope in a difficult situation?

____

5. Clearly the writer had in mind the transformation of all things when he wrote these verses. Read about it in Isaiah 51:6, 66:22; Revelation 6:14 and 21:1. How do these verses help you look beyond present difficulties and into the heart of God?

____

____

6. What do you feel God most wants to communicate to you through them?

____

____

I LISTEN

The writer of Hebrews needed Psalm 102:25-27 to explain Hebrews 1:2-3. The Son is eternal and through Him everything was created and sustained. Everything said of God is now applied to Jesus Christ. The Son has no beginning and no end. This can never be said of angels whose beginning dates from the moment God created them. Jesus is almighty, unchangeable, and eternal.

Actually, Psalm 102 is the prayer of a believer overwhelmed with trouble. He longs to be in Zion. But he can't be, so he pours out his hurt and longing. As he writes his feelings out to God, something happens. God begins to pour His comfort in. This hurting man's prayer turns into a song of praise of the power and unchangeableness of God.

Write your own feelings out to God. Be honest before Him.

WE TALK TOGETHER

Just as the psalmist turned his pain into praise, so can you. Allow God to transform your hurts and disappointments into a song addressed to your Unchangeable God. As you give Him praise, He will give you hope.

❦ DAY 5 ❦

GOD SPEAKS

THE TRIUMPHANT SON

Read **Hebrews 1:13-14.**

1. The command to "sit at My right hand," describes an oriental court with two seats, one on the left hand, one on the right. The one on the right is the most honorable. Who has been asked by God Himself to sit there?

____

2. What does this tell you about how the Father feels about the work Christ completed on the cross?

____

____

The King, seated on His throne, is surrounded by servants standing ready to do His bidding. To be asked to sit at the King's right hand at any time was the greatest honor one could ever hope to receive. To be asked to sit while He was on the throne spoke of rank and power. Jesus sat as no angel had ever sat.

But the writer isn't finished with his word picture. The phrase, "Your enemies Your footstool" describes an oriental military practice. A king or general would place his feet on the neck of a defeated king to show that he had triumphed.

3. Read more about this heavenly scene in **Revelation 4**. What kind of response does it arouse inside you?

____

4. Although Jesus is shown seated on the throne, that doesn't mean He's not actively involved on our behalf.

Called to Maturity

a. What did Stephen see before he was stoned to death (Acts 7:56)?

____

b. What does Jesus say He is doing in John 14:1-4?

____

c. In John 17:20-26?

____

d. In 1 Corinthians 15:25?

____

e. What encouragement do these verses give you?

____

From God's throne, commands are given to the angels to minister to us. Even archangels are sent by God to work on behalf of His saints (Luke 1:11-38; Jude 9). Look up as many of the following scriptures as you have time for.

5. List the ways angels serve those who inherit salvation:

a. **Daniel 8:15-19**

____

b. **1 Kings 19:5, 7**

____

c. **Ezekiel 9:1**

____

d. **Zechariah 1:12-13**

____

6. Even though angels are important, they're not as important as Jesus Christ. Quickly compare the number of references to Jesus and to angels in your concordance. What do you discover?

____

____

____

7. How important is Jesus Christ to you? On a scale of 1-10, how does He rate?

____

Challenge activity: In your notebook, jot down seven facts you discovered this week about angels. About Jesus Christ. Use these facts to write a paragraph that shows how God's relationship to the Son is different from His relationship with His angels.

I LISTEN

Do an acrostic that compares angels and Jesus.

A	J
N	E
G	S
E ager to worship	U nderstanding Lord
L	S
S	

WE TALK TOGETHER

Read Psalm 110:1-3. Although this is written about Jesus Christ on the throne, the last sentence is for us, too. Read Isaiah 40:29-31 and Hosea 14:5-7. Our Lord wants to renew our strength. He wants to do it day by day. All we need to do is ask Him.

Called to Maturity

WALKING ALONG TOGETHER

More than anything else, I wanted to be an angel when I went to heaven. In my seven-year-old thinking, nothing could be more desirable than flying through space with unfurled wings.

Sometimes I put on my mother's white flannel nightgown and flew around the living room, my arms outstretched, my white draperies swirling around my ankles.

Oh, to be an angel. I could sit on top of a fluffy cloud. The wind would touch my cheeks and earth would be far, far below. I could hardly wait.

I tried to put my dream into words to my mother.

She frowned. "But, honey, you can't be an angel. You're going to be a saint."

A saint! I didn't know what a saint was, but one thing I did know. I didn't want to be one—ever—period. I wanted to be an angel.

One day my brother, Dale, said he saw an angel standing in the front yard. Hurt stabbed me. *Why him and not me?* After that I looked for angels in the yard, especially at twilight. Somehow that seemed the right time for angel appearances. I also looked for angels in the woods, in the barn, and even in the granary. I never found one. Angels seemed more mysterious than ever.

That I would be a saint and not an angel was a great disappointment. Even now I feel a sense of wonder—and, yes, a bit of envy, too—when I picture them around God's throne. The rainbow, the lightning, the expanse of glass. Yet all these pale before the splendor of my Lord. What must it be like to behold His face? To worship Him?

I know now that the angels' splendor in no way equals that of the Son. Although they worship at His throne and do His bidding, they are mere servants sent to minister to those who are heirs of salvation.

The Superiority of Christ

As I open my Bible to the first chapter of Hebrews, I feel anticipation. *Jesus Christ, superior, better, more excellent than the angels.*

I know from my studies that the Jews considered angels as mediators between God and man. At the time Hebrews was written, humankind had been impressed with the transcendence of God. Instead of feeling close to Him, they felt more and more distant. God was unknowable, they said. He's unreachable. God does not speak to humans, humans can't speak to Him. They began to believe that God spoke through angels, that angels brought humans' prayers into God's presence.

No wonder the writer of Hebrews went to such length to show the people that Jesus was superior to angels. Angels are beautiful but there is no need for them to be between God and His child.

I search for more truth from the various psalms the writer used to prove that Jesus is greater than the angels. Jesus Christ fulfilled the words of Psalm 45. He is the King and in His hand He holds the scepter of righteousness—the King has authority to hold out the scepter to anyone He invites to approach His throne.

He's holding His scepter out to me. He's inviting me to come. Because of Jesus' death on the cross, I can come directly into God's presence. I don't need any supernatural being to go there for me.

I reach for my journal. *Lord Jesus, I love you. Because of Your love for righteousness the Father has anointed You with the oil of gladness.*

Drawing Near

As I draw near, I'm aware of the spices of heaven—myrrh, aloes, and cassia—that cling to His robes. There's music. Is it the angels' songs that make His heart rejoice?

I hear His voice. "Listen, O Eva, consider and incline your ear."

I write, *Lord, I'm listening. You want me to focus on You and You alone right now.*

A stillness gradually wraps around my spirit. I am His princess, dressed in a garment of righteousness—His righteousness. He's drawing me close to His heart.

Verses 13-14 from the *New American Standard Bible* sparkle at me. "The King's daughter is all glorious within; her clothing is interwoven with gold. She will be led to the King in embroidered work; the virgins, her companions who follow her, will be brought to Thee. They will be led forth with gladness and rejoicing; they will enter into the King's palace."

John writes that we, "have an anointing from the Holy One . . . . The anointing you have received from Him abides in you" (1 John 2:20, 27).

I am His daughter. His queen. His heavenly fragrance permeates my heart and I am beautiful. Anointed. Set apart for Him.

This anointing is something the angels don't have. This oil of gladness is only for the Son and those who've experienced new life in Him—the saints.

Called to Maturity

Sometimes I think about my mother's words that long ago day. "But, honey, you're not going to be an angel. You're a saint."

And saints are heirs of all things. I smile to myself. *Saint Eva. Yes, that's me.*

And Saint Eva with all the other saints is going to one day kneel before God's throne. Underneath my knees will be a sparkling expanse of glass, but instead of mirroring me, I'll see the Son. Because I'm an heir of His salvation, I'll be a reflection of who He is.

Because I have His anointing I press on toward spiritual maturity. Part of that pressing on is lingering in His presence.

3

A Warning to Heed

Hebrews 2:1-4

DAY 1

GOD SPEAKS

THE DANGER OF DRIFTING

Read **Hebrews 2:1-4**.
The word *drift* is key in our study of this passage.

1. Imagine that you're a boat moored at a dock. As the current tugs, your knot loosens. Almost without realizing it you're adrift, alone on the river. Describe some of the problems you might have. Where might you end up?

2. Read one or more additional translations of Hebrews 2:1 if you have access to them. Look up *drift* in a dictionary, then write your own definition of the word.

3. The danger of drifting is real. William Barclay gives a compelling description of the words *pay attention to* (give the more earnest heed to) and *drift*. Underline words, phrases, and/or sentences that are significant.

> In the first verse there may be an even more vivid picture than there is in the translation which we have used. The two key words are *prosechein* and *pararrein*. We have taken *parachein* to mean to pay attention to, which is one of its commonest meanings. *Pararrein* is a word of many meanings. It is used of something flowing or slipping past; it can be used of a ring that has slipped off the finger. . . .
>
> But both of these words have also a nautical sense. *Prosechein* can mean to *moor a ship*; and *pararrein* can be used of a ship which has been carelessly allowed to slip past a harbour or a haven because the mariner has forgotten to allow for the wind or the current or the tide. So, then, this first verse could be very vividly translated: "Therefore, we must the more eagerly anchor our lives to the things that we have been taught lest the ship of life drift past the harbour and be wrecked."[1]

1. William Barclay, *The Letter to the Hebrews*, rev. ed., The Daily Study Bible Series (Philadelphia, PA: Westminster Press, 1976) p. 21.

4. There are a number of admonitions in Hebrews. List those you find in the following verses. One is already done for you.

   2:1-4 ______________________________

   3:1 ______________________________

   3:12-19 "Beware, brethren"

   4:1-3 ______________________________

   4:11 ______________________________

   4:14-16 ______________________________

5. What do these admonitions tell you about the heart of the writer towards his readers?

   ____

   ____

6. Try to put the message of these admonitions into one sentence. Example: Be true to your faith no matter what.

   ____

   ____

I LISTEN (Journaling Suggestion)

Look back at your description of the drifting boat. Compare the drifting boat to a Christian who is drifting away from God. What speaks most directly to you? What can you do to avoid a similar peril?

WE TALK TOGETHER (Prayer)

Ask God to examine your heart. Are there areas in your life where you feel the tug of the world? Write your response to Hebrews 2:l in a prayer. "Lord, I feel inside me a tendency to drift. I . . ."

❦ DAY 2 ❦

GOD SPEAKS

PAY CLOSE ATTENTION

Read **Hebrews 2:1-4**.

1. Has anyone ever given you a warning that you failed to pay attention to? What happened? Has anyone given you a warning that you did pay attention to? Which of these warnings produced the greatest benefit?

2. Anytime we observe transition words, such as "therefore," we need to look back at what was written in the preceding scripture passage—the warning not to drift flows from the context of Hebrews 1. What reasons do you find in this chapter to encourage you to pay close attention to the Son?

3. How might these reasons keep you from the perils of drifting?

Students of the Word have observed that Hebrews 2:1-4 is almost like a giant parenthesis placed between Hebrews 1:14 to 2:5. The writer uses this parenthesis technique five times throughout the book. They almost interrupt the flow. But if we view these rough spots as warning signs that surface, submerge, then surface again, they make more sense.

4. Five observations Bible students have made are listed below. Read them, then write down five of your own. Look for repeated words, rhetorical questions, strong verbs. The way our God communicates to us in His Word deserves our closest attention.
   1. Paying attention is emphasized by "must" and "much"
   2. Salvation can be neglected
   3. Author includes himself in the warning (us)
   4. What happened to angels can happen to us
   5. Personal pronoun, *we*, used five times
   6. ______________________________
   7. ______________________________
   8. ______________________________
   9. ______________________________
   10. ______________________________

I LISTEN

Questions triggered by Hebrews 2:1-4: Why is the *we* in verse 2 significant? What is it we are in danger of drifting into? What is the antidote for drifting?

Try to answer these questions. As you do, remember that the Hebrew Chrisians who received this letter were in danger of drifting away from what they'd been taught. Drifting can happen to anyone at any age, at whatever stage she may be in her spiritual journey through life.

It can happen to you.

WE TALK TOGETHER

Drifting appears to be an early step whereby one begins to neglect her salvation.

"Lord Jesus, because You are so important, I want to be on guard against the danger of slowly and carelessly slipping away from what I've heard about You in chapter one. The one truth I want to hold in my thoughts today is . . ."

DAY 3

GOD SPEAKS

A COMMITMENT TO HEAR

1. Imagine that you are working on this study in the family room while your husband and children watch *Star Wars*. All of a sudden your eight-year-old turns to you and says, "Hey, Mom, wasn't that neat?" You nod absently. After all, you've been sort of following the story. But do you really know what it was your child thought was so neat? Were you really listening?

   ____

2. One way to guard against drifting is to choose to hear and apply God's Word. *Cruden's Concordance* has this to say about the word *hear*: "This word is often used for listening to the Word of God with a firm purpose to obey His commands."[2]

   Read the parable of the two builders (Matt. 7:24-27). Compare this parable to Proverbs 14:1. How are these pictures similar?

   ____

   ____

   How are they different?

2. Alexander Cruden, A.M., *Cruden's Complete Concordance*, (New York, NY: Holt, Rinehart, and Winston, 1930), p. 286.

3. How could this house-tearing-down woman in Proverbs be an illustration of someone neglecting the "great salvation" in Hebrews 2:3?

4. Over and over God entreats us to "hear," to "listen." Can you think of other scriptures that talk about listening and hearing? Find and read them. Which one speaks most deeply to your own heart?

5. Look up words that have to do with hearing and listening under *hear* and *listen* in your concordance. Note the many "hear" scripture references in the New Testament. Jesus has lots to say in the Gospels about hearing and listening. Look up several of these references. Which ones were most helpful? Why?

I LISTEN

Spend some time today listening to God's Spirit speak to your heart. Turn off the T.V., the radio, silence the ringer on the phone.

Called to Maturity

After you've simply sat in His presence for a little while, write down your impressions, thoughts, and insights. What did you learn about listening with your heart? What did you learn about yourself? About your Lord?

WE TALK TOGETHER

Sing the chorus, "Open My Eyes, Lord" as a prayer of worship.

❦ DAY 4 ❦

GOD SPEAKS

A GREAT PAIN AND A GREAT SALVATION

Read **Hebrews 2:2-4.**

1. Although all of us are in danger of drifting, we're more susceptible at certain times. Which of the following holds the greatest danger for you right now?
   Too much to do
   Too many places to go
   Lack of direction and/or goals
   Little or no accountability
   Unresolved emotional pain
   An ongoing crisis
   Other:

   ____

   ____

Reread **Hebrews 2:2-3**. The argument here is from the lesser to the greater. If the law given to God's people by the angels brought pain to those who disobeyed it, how much greater is the grief that will come to those who neglect God's plan of salvation given in His Word?

2. Have you ever experienced the pain that comes from neglecting God's Word? Have you been close to someone who has? What did you learn from it?

3. Read the account of David's sin with Bathsheba (2 Sam. 11:1-27) as an example of one man's drift away from God's law (Deut. 5:17, 18, 21). Chart his drift in the following verses:
2 Samuel 11:1
2 Samuel 11:2
2 Samuel 11:3
2 Samuel 11:4
2 Samuel 11:6-13
2 Samuel 11:14-17
2 Samuel 11:27

Read **2 Samuel 12:10-12.**

4. What were the consequences of David's sin?

Reread **Hebrews 2:3-4**. The writer of Hebrews distinguishes the salvation he writes about from the many kinds of salvation offered in the ancient world by calling it, "such a great salvation." He tells us three things about it.

a. It was "spoken by the Lord" (Luke 19:9).

b. "Confirmed by those who heard it"—the first hearers to whom the Gospel was entrusted including the disciples (Luke 1:2).

c. "God also bearing witness" through supernatural acts of healing (Acts 3:7-9, 11-12, 16) and through supernatural gifts of the Holy Spirit (Acts 2:4-12).

5. Jot down three more things that you could say to someone about this "great salvation."

____

____

____

I LISTEN

The phrase, "[distributed] according to His will" (Heb. 2:4) takes on new meaning when we compare it to 1 Corinthians 12:4-11. Which of these gifts have you seen at work in the body you worship with? Which one do you believe is God's special gift to you?

WE TALK TOGETHER

Include the truths you discovered in Hebrews 2:4 in a prayer of praise. Be sure to include the phrase "so great a salvation." Thank God for what He's done for you!

❦ DAY 5 ❦

GOD SPEAKS

A REMINDER

1. If you had a friend who was drifting away from the things she'd been taught in God's Word, what would you say? What might you do to help her change course?

____

____

____

Read **2 Peter 1:12-14**.

2. Sometimes we feel that we always need to have some new truth from God's Word to share with others. But what is Peter saying in these verses?

Read **Hebrews 1-2:4.**

3. Jot down specific truths that you could remind your friend of that could make a difference in her life. What truth about the person of Jesus Christ do you think she might need most right now?

4. What truth do you need most right now—today?

Challenge activity: One of the ways we can keep from drifting is to set our mind on things above rather than the things of the earth. Read Colossians 3:1-17. Make a list of the characteristics of a mind set on earthly things, another list of the characteristics of a mind set on things above.

I LISTEN

The five warnings in Hebrews are highly visual. Draw a warning sign or symbol to illustrate Hebrew 2:1-4. Pray about sharing your drawing with a friend or family member who might be starting to drift in her Christian life.

WE TALK TOGETHER

Are there those in your family or church family who seem to be drifting away from what they have heard in God's Word? Pray for each one of them by name.

WALKING ALONG TOGETHER

I looked down at my Bible on my lap. I almost didn't want to open it. And yet—yesterday's time in the Word had been so real—so wonderful. Jesus Christ, exalted King, Creator of the world, the angels worshipping at His feet.

A reluctance, hard even to put into thoughts, tugged at my soul. Soon Paula would be coming—we meet each week to share our studies in Hebrews and pray together. But today I wouldn't be ready.

I looked out the window—pouring rain. Always when I was a child, whenever it rained, I'd be out in it tracking down tiny rivelets swollen into streams. I'd toss in a leaf and run alongside. How soon before the leaf went down? How long before it was caught by an overhanging limb?

I slipped into my blue rain jacket and out the door. Rain splashed my face as I hurried toward the creek. I heard it before I saw it—rushing, hurrying. Quiet eddies were moving faster now. The water was browner and higher.

As I came close, I picked up a winter-worn oak leaf and tossed it into the creek. For a moment it lingered near the bank, twirling idly. I watched fascinated. How long before the current lured it from its safe harbor? How long before it started its race to the river? Before it went down . . . down . . . and under?

The Reason

And suddenly I knew what I was trying to push away. *Mary Ellen.* When I'd seen her yesterday in the supermarket parking lot I'd hardly recognized her. Her black hair looked as though she'd run her fingers through it too many times. There were dark circles under her eyes.

Her words reached out to me. "Eva, I need to talk."

We got into the front seat of her car.

Mary Ellen's slim fingers toyed with the steering wheel. Her voice was scarcely audible. "Eva, I've been unfaithful to Daniel."

Her story came out in bits and pieces. "I wanted to talk to Daniel about Gerald. . . . Somehow the words wouldn't come. . . .

"All the time Gerald and I kept getting closer. And then it happened. Eva, I didn't mean mean for it to go that far. It just did . . ."

I felt numb when I climbed out of her car and headed home. I still felt that way. Except now the hurt was starting to hit. "Lord, how could she?"

I looked at the brown water. My leaf was moving away. In a little while the current would take it. Soon it would drift further and further and further away.

All of a sudden I couldn't stand it. The muddy bank slurped at my tennis shoes but I paid no attention. I broke off the slender end of a vine maple branch and reached as far as I could.

"Lord," I cried, "show me how to help Mary Ellen. I love her. I know she loves you, too."

My leaf eluded me. I leaned forward—snagged it. Carefully, I pulled it to shore, the wet leaf was safe in my hands at last.

It stayed cupped in my hands as I hurried home. I lay the leaf on my desk, shed my raincoat, and reached for my Bible. The warning words of Hebrews 2 jumped off the page and into my heart. "We must give the more earnest heed to the things we have heard, lest we drift away."

More Careful Attention

The Amplified Bible says, "Since all this is true, we ought to pay more careful attention than ever to the truths that we have heard, lest in any way we drift past {them} and slip away."

Later that morning Paula and I talk about sex and temptation. "Sometimes the secret lives Christians lead scares me," Paula says. "A friend I saw several times a week had an affair and I didn't even know it. And then there was Randy—he seemed like the perfect husband, godly, considerate—he almost broke Jenelle's heart. He was sexually involved with two different women in his office. Neither one knew about the other."

I nod. "I remember Rick—he's a minister now—telling Bud how he and his brother used to read pornographic magazines. For years they hid them in a crawl space above the bathroom. Their mother was a godly woman—she had no idea. At least not until the ceiling above the tub gave way and all the filth came tumbling down."

We laugh, but I'm thinking about my own children. Do they have hidden worlds they keep from me and my husband? They seem like good kids and yet . . . we're all so vulnerable.

"Paula," I say. "I've been tempted and it wasn't love for my husband that kept me from entering a secret world of lust and deceit. Nor was it love for my children—my church family—."

"Respect for yourself then?"

I shake my head. "Even thinking about what the consequences might be didn't have power to stop me."

"What then?"

"My love for my Lord. I knew from His Word how He felt about sexual immorality. Because I did—I—I just couldn't do it. I loved

Him too much. I still do. . . ."

For a moment we're silent.

We Can All Be Tempted

"What scares me is that I know how easy it is for love to grow cold. To drift away from the love that right now is my anchor. Paula, I can be tempted. I can drift. . . ."

"Sometimes I think the greatest thing we can do for one another is to simply remind each other who Jesus is," Paula says softly. "When we fall in love with Him with *all* our hearts—why—it's that love and commitment that will keep us from drifting into sin."

Love. Commitment.

Phrases in Hebrews 2 take on fresh significance. "Give the more earnest heed . . . lest we drift away. . . ." "How shall we escape if we neglect so great a salvation?"

I reach for my notebook, begin to write: *If the words of the law brought judgment and grief to those who heard it, how much greater the consequences for believers who neglect God's plan of salvation, spoken and delivered by God's own Son, the Lord Jesus Christ?*

The issue here is not whether or not believers have God revelation. It's rather, Are they neglecting it by failing to live truth they have already heard? Slowly drifting, a little at a time, away from what they've been taught in the beginning?

My words change into a prayer. *Lord, I know how vulnerable I am. Please, help me pay close attention to Your Word so that I won't drift into dangerous situations and compromise my faith.*

And please, Lord. help me know how to minister to Mary Ellen.

My damp brown leaf is on the desk. I pick it up, place it between two sheets of paper. My concordance goes on top. My dictionary.

Later I'll put my pressed leaf inside my Bible. It will remind me to stand fast, to persevere, to hold out a lifeline to other drifters.

I look forward to what I'll be learning tomorrow. Truth that will help me grow up. Truth that will help me stand true to my Lord. Truth that will help me reach out to Mary Ellen, to other believers, to my own family.

Lord, help me understand and apply Your Word.

4

• • •

Focusing on Jesus

Hebrews 2:5-18

❦ DAY 1 ❦

GOD SPEAKS

WHAT IS MAN?

Read **Hebrews 2:5-9**.

1. What are some words and/or phrases that come to your mind when you think of mankind in general?

____

____

____

Called to Maturity

2. Last week we studied the giant parenthesis placed between Hebrews 1:14 and 2:5. To see the flow of thought more clearly, write out 1:14 and 2:5. How does it make you feel to realize that humankind, not the angels, can inherit salvation?

____

Angels can't inherit salvation, neither have they been given dominion over the earth. Humankind has.

Read **Genesis 1:27-30.**

3. In what ways do we see humans' dominion over the earth?

____

____

4. In what ways has he failed to exercise dominion?

____

____

The writer quotes from Psalm 8:4-6 to illustrate the glory of humankind. This psalm sings with the majesty with which God crowned His creation. It is the glory God means for each one of us to have.

5. Compare and contrast Psalm 8:3-6 with Hebrews 2:6-8. Write down five observations from each passage. What is the same? What is different or expanded?

____

____

____

____

From this ideal picture the writer turns to the reality of what sin has done to humankind. Although we've been crowned with nobility, greatness, and dignity, we're frustrated because of the Fall (Gen. 3:16-19).

6. Match the following with verses from Hebrews 2:5-9 wherein the writer shows us . . .

   . . . what man should be ______________________________

   . . . what man really is ______________________________

   . . . how Jesus can make man what man was meant to be

   ____

It is by the grace of God that the Father allowed His Son to suffer for the redemption of sinful man.

I LISTEN (Journaling Suggestion)

There is majesty in our salvation. Paul expresses this in his prayer for the Ephesian believers (Eph. 1:15-29)—that they might know His majesty . . . His incomparable power . . . His supreme rule and authority. Choose one key thought from these verses. Explore your response to it in your journal.

WE TALK TOGETHER (Prayer)

Spend time praising Jesus for His majesty. Begin and end your prayer and praise time with the words the psalmist used. (Ps. 8:1, 9): "O Lord, our Lord, how excellent is Your name in all the earth!"

❦ DAY 2 ❦

GOD SPEAKS

WHO ARE YOU, JESUS?

Read **Hebrews 2:9-11**.

1. For most of us there have been people who have gone ahead of us, showing the way to God. Perhaps it was a grandparent, a neighbor, a teacher. How did your special person point you to Jesus?

   ____

   ____

2. The people to whom this letter was addressed needed someone to help them focus on Jesus. They were tired, ready to quit. They hurt. Then in one long significant sentence, the writer reveals Jesus crowned and Jesus crucified (Heb. 2:9). How could this two-fold truth give them hope?

   ____

   ____

   How could it give you hope?

   ____

   ____

The way God is revealed in a particular book tells us a lot about the one who wrote it. That Jesus was true man as well as true God meant much to the writer—he calls the Savior by His human name, Jesus, nine times in Hebrews. Note the phrase "But we see Jesus" in verse 9.

3. Look up the other eight references to Jesus and write down the significant truth that directly refers to Jesus.

2:9 ______________________________

3:1 ______________________________

4:14 ______________________________

6:20 ______________________________

7:22 ______________________________

10:19-20 ______________________________

12:2 ______________________________

12:24 ______________________________

13:12 ______________________________

Put a star by the truth that speaks to you most directly. Be ready to share it with someone.

Sometimes when we're studying a passage of scripture we need to stop and pay particular attention to a single word in order to better understand the fullness of truth God has for us. *Author* in verse 10 is like that. Here the writer to the Hebrews uses one of the great titles of Jesus. In the original Greek He calls Jesus the *archēgos* of glory.

Other words that help us understand what *archēgos* means are "pioneer," "head," "chief," "founder," or "originator."

Barclay has this to say:

> An *archēgos* is one who blazes the trail for others to follow. Someone has used this analogy. Suppose a ship is on the rocks, and suppose the only way to rescue is for someone to swim ashore with a line in order that, once the line was secured, others might follow. The one who is first to swim ashore would be the *archēgos* of the safety of the others. This is what the writer to

the Hebrews means when he says that Jesus is the *archēgos* of our salvation. Jesus has blazed the trail to God for us to follow.[1]

Another significant word is *perfect*. The basic meaning of perfect—the Greek word, *teleioun*—is not so much to make perfect, as to make fully adequate for, able for, the task or the plan for which the person is designed.

4. How did Jesus' suffering make Him fully able to be the pioneer of your salvation?

____

____

I LISTEN

The word *teleios*, translated "perfect" in Hebrews 2:10, is translated as "mature" in James 1:2-4 in the NIV. Can you relate this maturity to a plant that has gone through the complete cycle of maturity and is now producing fruit? Draw a picture of this cycle, then turn to Galatians 5:22-23. Which of these godly characteristics do you want most to ripen into maturity in your life? Talk to God about it in your journal.

WE TALK TOGETHER

Considering hard things as joy doesn't come easily to any of us. But the joy that comes by focusing on Jesus is a real part of Christian maturity. Address your prayer to Jesus, the Author and Pioneer of your salvation. What He has begun in you, He will complete. He's beside you, helping you grow up.

---

1. William Barclay, *The Letter to the Hebrews*, rev. ed., The Daily Study Bible Series (Philadelphia, PA: Westminster Press, 1976), p. 26.

DAY 3

GOD SPEAKS

JESUS, OUR BROTHER

Read **Hebrews 2:11-13.**

Two men were in a prison camp during World War 2. During the day they foraged for greens to add to the watery soup the Germans brought them each evening. At night they talked about the families they'd left behind. The suffering they shared forged a bond that lasted a lifetime. Whenever one talked about the other, he always said, "My brother. . ."

1. Have you ever shared a deep hurt with another person? What effect did it have on your relationship?

____

____

____

Jesus became a man in order to identify with a lost and suffering world (Luke 19:10). Only by His death on the cross was He able to restore sinful man to be the people He created them to be. The footnote in the *NIV Study Bible* says, "Our brotherhood with Jesus is the brotherhood of the Redeemer with the redeemed, who are truly one with him."

2. What does it mean to you to realize that Christ, the Son of God, seated at the right hand of the majesty in heaven, is not ashamed to call Himself your brother? That you can call Him your brother?

____

____

Called to Maturity

Read **Psalm 22.** (This psalm is quoted more frequently in the New Testament than any other psalm.) Although this psalm is David's own cry for deliverance, it vividly describes Christ's suffering on the cross.

3. Compare the following verses and write down your observations.
   Psalm 22:1a **Matthew 27:46**

   Psalm 22:18 **Matthew 27:35**

   Psalm 22:22 **Hebrews 2:12**

Through His sacrificial death, Jesus identifies with us. Together we form the family of God—the Church.

The writer next quotes Isaiah 8:17 as words from Jesus' own lips. "I will hope in Him." And again, "He says, 'Here am I, and the children whom God has given Me'" (Heb. 2:13). The context is important. Chapters 7-9 of Isaiah are messianic chapters. The birth of a son is mentioned in Isaiah 7:14-17 and 8:1-4.

4. What name for Jesus is given in Isaiah 7:14?

5. How does this name fit in with what you are learning about Jesus in Hebrews 2?

I LISTEN

Christ is in the midst of His people. And where Christ is, there is song. Read Zephaniah 3:16-17. Put in your own name for Zion.

Jesus Himself is drawing near to you. He's singing. Paraphrase the truth you've learned this week into a song from His own lips to you. Write it in your journal.

WE TALK TOGETHER

Now it's your turn. Write your song response back to Him.

❦ DAY 4 ❦

GOD SPEAKS

JESUS, OUR POWERFUL HELPER

Read **Hebrews 2:14-18.**

1. Have you ever heard the phrase, "blood is thicker than water"? What does it mean?

   ____

In earlier verses the writer of Hebrews has shown us that Jesus and his followers belong to the same family—He is our blood relative. The ties that bind us to Him are blood ties—He is our brother.

2. According to Hebrews 2:14-15 what two things happened as a result of His death?

   a. ______________________________

   b. ______________________________

The term *bond slave* was contemporary to those living at the time the book of Hebrews was written. Being a slave meant you weren't free to make your own decisions. It meant someone besides yourself could tell you what to do and see that you did it.

3. How do you think these Christians felt when they read verse 15?

____

How does it make you feel to realize that you have an Elder Brother with greater power than your greatest enemy?

____

Propitiation (atonement) is a significant idea in this passage. God's wrath was directed toward us because of sin—it separated us from God.

In the Old Testament the High Priest on the Day of Atonement entered the Holy of Holies where he sprinkled blood for his own sin and that of the people. In the same way, Jesus, the sinless Son of God, offered himself so that His shed blood covered our sins. He, as our High Priest, brought God and man together in perfect harmony (Rom. 5:1).

4. Someone has tried to simplify the word *atonement* by calling it "at-one-ment." Underline the word in the paragraph above that "at-one-ment" suggests.

Whenever we read a portion of scripture we can ask, "What does this show me about who God is?" Hebrews 2:11-13 shows Jesus as our Brother, verses 14-15 as our Deliverer, verse 17 as our High Priest.

5. What do verses 16 and 18 show Jesus as?

____

I LISTEN

The word *aid* (help) in Hebrews 2:16 means "to take hold of with a purpose," "to take by the hand." What kind of picture does this create in your mind?

Reflect on ways Jesus has fulfilled His role as someone who comes to your aid.

WE TALK TOGETHER

How has Jesus proved to be a helper to you this week? In what area do you need specific help today?

❦ DAY 5 ❦

GOD SPEAKS

JESUS, OUR HIGH PRIEST

Read **Hebrews 2:17-18**.

1. Look up the word *sympathize* in a dictionary. Is it possible to sympathize with someone's suffering if you haven't gone through the same sorrow yourself?

   ____

2. Compare **Hebrews 2:16-18** to **Hebrews 4:14-16**. Write down five observations from each passage.

   Hebrews 2:16-18 **Hebrews 4:14-16**

   a. ______________________________

   b. ______________________________

   c. ______________________________

   d. ______________________________

   e. ______________________________

Jesus' identification with us is an important concept in chapter 2 and is repeated in verses 9, 14, 15. Now the writer makes his first mention of Jesus as our High Priest. Verse 17 tells us Jesus had to become man in order to fulfill that role. Here only two of His high-priestly characteristics are mentioned—mercy and faithfulness.

3. How would you describe mercy?

____

Faithfulness?

____

Challenge activity: Look up *mercy* and *faithfulness* in a dictionary. Do the same with *atonement*. Pick out phrases that best match the biblical meaning of each word.

I LISTEN

The response of Christ to those who are being tempted is seen in the the phrase "able to aid those" (v. 18). In the Greek it means to, "run to the (our) cry."

Tempted to give in? Tempted to give up? Tempted to run away? But wait. All we have to do is cry out to Him. When we do, He runs to help us.

Name one temptation you have experienced this week. Now picture Jesus Christ running to your side. What does He want to do for you? What is your response to Him?

WE TALK TOGETHER

Ask God to bring to your mind a particular temptation that you need His help to overcome. See Jesus run to you as you lift that particular temptation to Him.

WALKING ALONG TOGETHER

I'll never forget the winter I was nine. That was the year Daddy bought our John Deere tractor.

I can still remember the excitement I felt as Mother, Daddy, Dale, Lawrence, and I crowded around the kitchen table, the John Deere catalog open in front of us. "Picture yourself on this seat," the caption commanded and that was just what my older brother, Lawrence, was doing.

That spring Daddy got down the red cigar box and counted out the bills. We could hardly believe it. That wonderful tall green John Deere tractor would be ours. No longer would we have to hire the neighbor to plow our garden plot. No longer would Daddy have to scythe the hay by hand. We would have a tractor and all our needs would be met.

That summer John Deere came to live with us. With Lawrence at John's wheel, fields were plowed and disked and harrowed. Dale, and I even got into the act. We rode atop the harrow and the disk as weights to help break up the dirt clods.

An Accident

One day when Dale and I were acting as weights an unexpected jounce tossed me from the top of the disk and onto the ground in front of it. I have no memory of my fall but I heard a horrible cry—it was my own voice. The tractor jerked to a stop.

The disk was on top of me and I saw my brother's face as he turned. He leaped from the tractor seat and lifted the disk from my back. I sprang out, unhurt.

"I'm all right," I said.

My shirt was uncut. Lawrence brushed dirt from it and then wiped my face with the corner of his. "I'll take you to Mother."

I shook my head. "I'm all right," I insisted.

My legs shook. My mouth tasted funny. But I had to get back on the disk again. I had to.

Lawrence understood. He smiled reassuringly as I climbed back up beside Dale.

When we rounded the corner of the field, we saw Mother hurrying toward us. We lifted our hands and waved.

Mother frowned.

We smiled.

We didn't come in until the field was free of clods.

Today I read Hebrews 2 and remembered the story I just told you. For some reason I had never before grasped with my heart that Jesus is my Elder Brother—that we're bonded together with a blood tie and a cord of love.

Part of the Same Family

Jesus has identified Himself with me. I've identified myself with Him. We really are part of the same family.

Called to Maturity

Later I read Hebrews 2 in *The Amplified Bible*: The last part of verse 18 brings tears to my eyes. "He is able (immediately) to run to the cry of (assist, relieve) those who are being tempted and tested and tried and who therefore are being exposed to suffering."

A cry and my Brother runs to me. He's beside me lifting the weight from off my back. He wipes off my dirt, pats my shoulder.

He understands my need to continue. We work together until the job is done.

I need to record what I'm learning about my Lord in my journal. I turn the pages slowly, thoughtfully. Words like *transcendence* and *imminence* dance in my mind.

Always before when I read those words I'd had a sense of God's loftiness. Maybe because those particular words seemed so scholarly and unknowable.

Not so today. Instead of writing I put what I see about Jesus in Hebrews into a drawing.

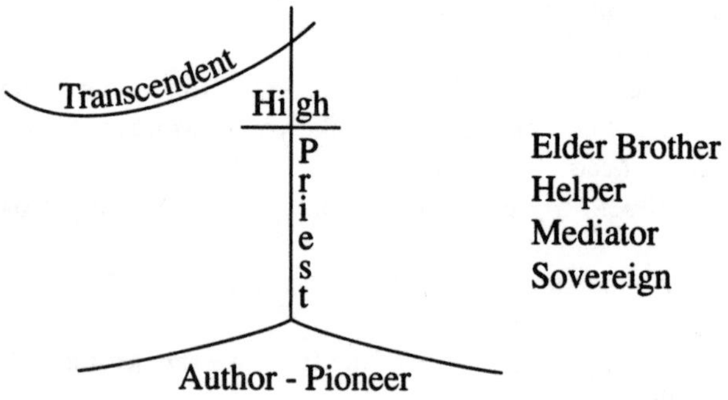

Underneath I write: *As special as my brother, Lawrence, is, he isn't adequate to meet all my needs. Only Jesus is.*

When I see Jesus crowned, I see His majesty and power. When I see Him crucified, I see His love. He is majestic, sovereign, the Pioneer of my salvation, my great High Priest, my Helper. I love Him.

I smile. *And I love Lawrence, too. I need to tell him so.*

5

• • •

Called to Faithfulness

Hebrews 3:1-6

❦ DAY 1 ❦

GOD SPEAKS

CONSIDER JESUS

Read **Hebrews 3:1-6.**

1. Has anyone ever told you that you had a fixation on something or someone? What did that person mean? Was it meant as a compliment or a criticism? Would you say that the object of our attention determines whether or not a fixation is a good thing?

____

____

____

Reread **Hebrews 3:1.**

2. Who is being addressed?

____

3. What important transition in verse 1 does the writer use to pull our thoughts back to Hebrews 2?

____

4. What important truth about Jesus in the closing verses of the previous chapter does it tie into?

____

5. Finish the following sentence: Because we have a merciful and faithful high priest who comes when we cry out, we are to . . .

____

6. In Hebrews 3:1 the writer calls his readers "holy brethren." How do you feel about being called a "holy brother"?

____

7. In the following translations of verse 1, underline the words that help you better understand what is meant by "holy brother."

> Therefore, holy brothers, who share the heavenly calling, fix your thoughts on Jesus, the apostle and high priest whom we confess (NIV).

> So then, brethren, consecrated and set apart for God, who share in the heavenly calling, thoughtfully and attentively consider Jesus, the Apostle and High Priest Whom we confessed as ours [when we embraced the Christian faith] (TAB).
>
> THEREFORE DEAR BROTHERS whom God has set apart for himself—you who are chosen for heaven—I want you to think now about this Jesus who is God's Messenger and the High Priest of our faith (TLB).

Read it again in the NIV. What words come to your mind when you think about the phrase, "fix your thought on"? Jot them down in your notebook.

Reread the translations of **Hebrews 3:1**. The Greek phrase for *consider* or *fix* has the sense of "to think deeply."

9. What do you see in this verse as you consider Jesus?

____

____

We find the same word used in the following scriptures. Read Hebrews 10:24, Luke 12:24, and Matthew 7:13. Consider the following excerpt by William Barclay.

> The word means to fix the attention on something in such a way that its inner meaning, the lesson that it is designed to teach, may be learned. In Luke 12:24 Jesus uses the same word when He says: "*Consider* the ravens." He does not merely mean, "*Look* at the ravens." He means, "Look at the ravens and *understand and learn* the lesson that God is seeking to teach you through them."[1]

The word *consider* means that we observe so closely that we appreciate and understand. In Matthew 7:13 it is used to describe the

---

1. William Barclay, *The Letter to the Hebrews*, rev. ed., The Daily Study Bible Series (Philadelphia, PA: Westminster Press, 1976), p. 29.

close scrutiny we'd use to find a speck in someone's eye; to focus with intensity.

I LISTEN (Journaling Suggestions)

Paraphrase **Hebrews 3:1**. (Paraphrase is simply putting God's Word into your own words so you can more fully understand it. *The Living Bible* is a paraphrase.)

Where it says *brethren,* write your name. (The term *holy brethren* communicates consecration and affection. These people are dear to the writer.)

Think deeply—consider—ponder—reflect on Jesus. Understand and learn what God is seeking to teach you through Him.

WE TALK TOGETHER (Prayer Suggestion)

Put what you're learning about Jesus into a prayer. He is the Apostle, the merciful and faithful High Priest. He loves you.

❦ DAY 2 ❦

GOD SPEAKS

WHO IS MOSES?

Read **Hebrews 3:2-6.**

1. Who on earth today do you consider to be the greatest man or woman?

____

The Jews held Moses in high esteem. He was the one to whom God gave the law and spoke with face to face. Moses stood between the Jews and God.

The readers to whom Hebrews was written were familiar with the words God spoke about Moses in Numbers 12:7-8b.

2. How would you have felt about a person whom God described in this way?

Jesus was faithful as Moses was faithful. Moses not only served the Israelites, he was willing for their sake to be blotted out of God's book.

Read **Exodus 32:30-32.**

3. What does this tell you about Moses?

---

4. Think about this in connection with Hebrews 3:1-6. What does it tell you about the trustworthiness of Jesus?

---

5. In Hebrews 1, we learned that Jesus is superior to the prophets. In Hebrews 2, that He is superior to the angels. How does Hebrews 3:1-6 continue and strengthen the theme of Hebrews: CHRIST IS SUPERIOR? Finish the sentence: Christ is superior to

---

6. Read verses 1-6 and write down 10-12 additional observations. Look for titles that pertain to Jesus, words that are repeated more than once. Note comparisons, proper names and specific nouns.

Called to Maturity

7. What similarities do you see between Moses and Jesus?

   a. ______________________________

   b. ______________________________

   c. ______________________________

   What contrasts do you see between them?

   a. ______________________________

   b. ______________________________

   c. ______________________________

8. What other similarities are there in Moses' and Jesus' ministries?

   ____

   ____

That Jesus and Moses have both been faithful to God is a great truth—one that we can take into our hearts—one that can change our lives.

9. Is there someone in your life that you could describe as a faithful person? How does faithfulness come out in their words and actions?

   ____

   ____

   ____

   ____

I LISTEN

Choose one of the following to explore in your journal:

1. How has Jesus' faithfulness been expressed to you personally this week?

2. In what area of your life, do you most feel the need to be more faithful?

WE TALK TOGETHER

Lamentations is probably the darkest book of the Bible. Yet God's faithfulness shines from its pages like a diamond on black velvet. Read Lamentations 3:22-26, then paraphrase the words to your faithful God, e.g. "LORD, your lovingkindness towards me never stops. It just keeps coming and coming. . . ."

❦ DAY 3 ❦

GOD SPEAKS

JESUS, BUILDER OF THE HOUSE

Read **Hebrews 3:2-6.**

1. If someone built a house for you, to whom would you address your thank you note? The house or the builder?

   ____

2. Fill in the following blanks: The term *house* is used ______ times in these ______ verses. When you hear someone say "the house of God," what comes into your mind?

   ____

3. It is interesting that the early believers never called a building God's house. Read the following verses and try to answer the questions.
   a. **1 Corinthians 3:16**: Who is the temple? How does God feel about this particular temple?

   ____

b. **1 Corinthians 6:19**: Who does this temple belong to?

____

What command is there here for believers today?

____

c. **2 Corinthians 6:16-17**: What kind of a temple are we to be?

____

What promise is there for the one who follows God's command in this verse?

____

d. **1 Peter 2:5**: What kind of house are we to be? What work are we to do?

____

I LISTEN

Houses begin with blueprints and God has one for you. Read Psalm 139:13-16. In what ways are you different from your husband? Your best friend? What talents do you have? What kind of personality? How does it make you feel to know that you are a one-of-a-kind living stone? That you have a special place in the church that only you can fill?

WE TALK TOGETHER

Use Psalm139:13-16 in a prayer of praise to the One who knit you together into such a complex and wonderful being while you were still in your mother's womb. Ask Him to show you ways that you can cultivate faithfulness in your relationship with Him and with others.

❦ DAY 4 ❦

GOD SPEAKS

THE SERVANT AND THE SON

Read **Hebrews 3:5-6.**

1. Describe the difference between a servant in a house and the son who is over the house? Be honest now, which would you really prefer to be? Explain why.

___

___

___

The contrast of Moses as the servant *in* God's house to Jesus as the Son *over* God's house further demonstrates Jesus' superiority to Moses. It also tells us more about Moses.

The writer of Hebrews uses the word *servant* to describe Moses. This word specifies one who is in service to someone who is their superior. It is not like a slave who must serve, but is descriptive of someone who wishes to serve.

2. On a scale of 1-10, how would you rate your desire to serve God?

___

Jesus was sent directly from God to be the Son over the Father's house.

Read **Matthew 21:33-40.**

3. How would you explain this parable? Who is the landowner? the vinedressers? the servants? the son?

___

Called to Maturity

____

____

____

In this parable, Jesus used the phrase of Himself—"Last of all, he sent his son to them, saying, 'They will respect my son,'" (Matt. 21:37).

When we consider that the writer to the Hebrews called "Jesus, the Apostle" (Heb. 3:1), which means one who is sent, and then "Christ is faithful as a son" (Heb. 3:6 NIV), we catch a vital truth. God sent His Son.

Read **Matthew 28:18-20.**

4. Through the sacrifice of the Son whom God sent, we who trust in Him are now sent directly by the Son.
   Where are we sent?

   ____

   What are we sent to do?

   ____

   To whom are we sent?

   ____

I LISTEN

The Father sent the Son into the world and the Son finished the work He was given to do. Before He ascended to take His place at the Father's right hand, He gave His followers instructions for service. Reflect on Jesus' words (Matt. 28:18-20) and then personalize them into a job description that fits you right where you are.

Is there a specific person that you feel God wants you to minister to in some way? A special task He wants you to do?

WE TALK TOGETHER

Ask your faithful God to give you the courage you need to follow through on what your heart tells you to do. Ask Him to make you His faithful servant.

❦ DAY 5 ❦

GOD SPEAKS

THE HOUSEHOLD OF GOD

Read **Hebrews 3:6**.

1. When you hear the word *church*, what kind of feelings well up inside you? What are some synonyms that come into your mind?

____

____

____

____

The writer of Hebrews makes a strong point when he says that "we are Christ's house." Although the world is God's house, it is the Church in particular—the family of God—that God built for His own special purposes (Eph. 2:19-22, 5:25-32; 1 Pet. 2:5; 1 Tim. 3:14-15).

2. Draw a sketch of the spiritual household described in Ephesians 2:19-22 and 1 Peter 2:5. The house rising from the foundation and the cornerstone is made up of individual stones, the people of God. Write various names onto the stones of those you know who have accepted Jesus Christ as their Savior.

____

____

Called to Maturity

The Body of Christ, the Church, is God's house. It will only stand firm when every stone in it is faithful to stay in its place.

> But Christ, the Messiah, was faithful over His [own Father's] house as a Son [and Master of it]. And it is we who are [now members of] this house, if we hold fast and firm to the end our joyful and exultant confidence and sense of triumph in our hope [in Christ] (Heb. 3:6 TAB).

The last clause begins with—"If we hold fast the confidence and the rejoicing of the hope firm to the end." It would almost seem that we, the stones, imprinted with Christ's own name—Christian—could roll off the house if we don't hold fast.

But that isn't the point the writer is making. Continuing faithful to the end proves our faith is for real. The household of God is made up of all kinds of believers. It's those who fail and sin and cry and keep turning to Jesus who continue on to the end.

3. Have you ever faced a severe disappointment? a tragedy? a lost ministry? How did God keep you from turning away from Him? Who or what did He use to give you the courage to continue faithful?

____

____

____

____

4. What word of encouragement could you give to someone who is going through something right now that is tempting them to stop following Jesus?

____

____

The very act of turning to God in our pain, validates our faith. It is an act of courage that strengthens the entire household of God and results in an exultant confidence and triumph. We have someone to boast about.

5. Complete the following names for Jesus from Hebrews 3:1-6: Jesus is . . .

   a. the A ______________________________

   b. H________________ P ________________

   c. C ________________________________

   d. a S ______________________________

Challenge activity: *The Amplified Bible* (Heb. 3:6) encourages us to hold fast and firm to the end "our joyful and exultant confidence and sense of triumph in our hope {in Christ}. Look up *exultant* and *triumph* in a dictionary. Do you know someone who has "exultant confidence" and "triumph" in Jesus? Interview her this week. What does she have to teach you about successful Christian living?

I LISTEN

It is significant that the name *Christ* is used for the first time in Hebrews 3:6. The sufferings of earth and the glories of heaven link together in the two names—Jesus and Christ. "But we see Jesus, who was made a little lower than the angels . . . crowned with glory and honor" (Heb. 2:9). Reflect on how the humanity of Jesus and Christ's authority as the anointed Messiah can give you courage and strength in a difficult situation.

WE TALK TOGETHER

Review **Hebrews 2:18**. How does this verse give you courage to cry out to Him for your own needs? For the needs of others?

WALKING ALONG TOGETHER

When I was about eight years old I discovered that the big fir tree at the edge of the garden was a wonderful place to play. It was underneath its spreading branches that I built my first farm.

Our farm had a creek flowing through it, so my farm had to have one. I took the hoe and scraped out a creek to wind in and out amongst the ferns. I carried rocks from the real creek up the hill and carefully placed them in the dry creek bed.

Afterwards I looked at my farm. My creek was beautiful. *But a farm has to have fences,* I decided.

I gathered sticks and poked them into the ground. A field for the cow to graze in, a patch of grass to become a field of hay. The tall sword ferns growing alongside the creek were really forests of trees—wonderful trees that bent and swayed in remarkable ways, a lovely place for deer and squirrels and birds to hide in.

I picked rose hips off the wild rose bushes for sheep, the tiny burrs from the burdock became hens. I cut a cow out of the Montgomery Ward catalog and backed it with cardboard so she could stand up in the pasture.

My brother, Lawrence, built a barn for me out of lumber scraps. A house followed. My farm was complete.

Or was it? No. What was most important was still missing. I needed a family to live in the house.

My Farm Family

The day I carried my paper dolls that I'd cut out of the Sears Roebuck and Wards catalogs was the day my farm became a real home. My favorites were Jo Ann with the shiny dark hair and her little brother, Prentis, in the striped red and white coveralls. I still remember Prentis with his thumb stuck in his mouth. He followed Jo Ann everywhere.

I loved the little family that I carried back and forth in a shoebox from my house to the farm. Sometimes I wonder what happened to them. I know that the spreading fir tree overhead grew taller and now the wind sings through the branches. The creek disappeared a long time ago. The fence posts dissolved into the dirt.

Another House

And I went on to other things.

I remember the house my husband and I built when our children were small. That house grew board by board. The big white kitchen range had a place of honor in the unfinished kitchen. For awhile there were curtains in place of cupboard doors. The floor was wood, there wasn't yet money for linoleum. In the bedrooms the walls were bare 2 x 4's and, except for an occasional drape, everyone could see everyone.

As important as that house was to us, it was the people who were most important. Our oldest son Dow—a happy two-year-old when we built the house—poked nails down a knothole. Beth lost a doll inside the walls . . . years later she remembered she'd put it there for safe keeping.

I smile. Children do grow up. They leave home and build houses of their own.

I turn in my Bible to Hebrews 3. "Every house is built by someone, but He who built all things is God" (v. 4). I put my finger in the page and go back to Genesis. In chapter one, I see God creating a perfect world. Except something is missing. As excellent and beautiful as His creation is He wants a family to make it complete. Adam—Eve . . . And later two little boys—Cain and Abel. Then other children—more boys and girls.

My Family

I remember the family I grew up in. There was my father and mother, my brothers, Dale and Lawrence. The family my husband and I raised included Beth, Dow, Clytie, Mark, Darren, and Leigh. And of course there was my long ago paper doll family—Jo Ann, Prentis. . . .

Families are important. They're important to me. They're important to you. Most of all they're important to God.

I return to Hebrews 3. My faithful God, Creator of the world—the Builder of the house—and that house is me. Except—it isn't just me He's building. He's building His Church. Each believer in it is a living stone carefully crafted according to His design.

Another day. Another memory. This time I'm on my way to school. My brother and I have to walk a mile on graveled country road to reach the bus stop. But we don't mind. The gravel rolls beneath our shoes and it isn't ordinary stones we're walking on. We know that if we look carefully enough we'll find rocks that will pass the lick test. When they did we put them in our pockets. Later we'd add them to our collections. I can see them now, a rosy colored stone that's a tiny piece of a sunset, a golden agate with an Indian wigwam outlined in orange, a green stone with a fern in its heart.

The Lord's Precious Stones

I open my journal. I like being reminded that I'm God's precious stone. That I'm a cherished part of the household of God. I sketch a rock on the page. But it needs a design, a special imprint of some kind—.

What do I look like anyway? My name is Christian.

My pencil presses hard. Now there's a cross on the rock. "And we are his house, if we hold on to our courage and the hope of which we boast" (v. 6 NIV).

Lord, I want to be faithful to You, as faithful as Moses was in all his house. I want to stand firm, to be faithful until the end—to continue on courageous—growing, risking, loving. . . .

I long to serve You—in my home—in the household of faith—even in the world. And someday, Lord, we'll be in heaven together. You and me.

I'll tell the saints how You ran to my side when I cried out for help. How You did it over and over.

I'll tell how You lifted me up when I fell down. How You never gave up on me.

But maybe—just maybe—I could tell a little bit now. After all, faithfulness begins with little things—the now things. And people are important.

I shut my notebook. *Lord, You've been putting Gail in my thoughts all week. And I'm part of Your family, the family of God. I have a new name and a faithful God. I have an exultant faith.*

I reach for the phone. I have Someone I can hardly wait to talk about. I need to find a time Gail and I can get together.

6

• • •

Called to Believe

Hebrews 3:7-19

❦ DAY 1 ❦

GOD SPEAKS

THE HOLY SPIRIT SPEAKS

Read **Hebrews 3:7-13**.

1. Respond to the following: "Personally knowing the author who wrote a book makes that book more significant." Why do you think this might be so?

Called to Maturity

2. We've already learned that God is the author of Scripture. The writers who put words on paper are only His spokesmen. Who does the writer say is speaking in **Hebrews 1:5-6**?

____

Hebrews 2:12-13?

____

Hebrews 3:7-11?

____

3. What does this tell you about the human writer?

____

____

Psalm 95 is quoted by the writer of Hebrews as words spoken by the Holy Spirit—David as the human author isn't even mentioned until later (Heb. 4:7).

Read **Psalm 95:7-11** and **Hebrews 3:7-9.**

4. How do these scripture passages show that Scripture is divinely inspired and speaks to people in every generation?

____

____

____

The writer of Hebrews held the Old Testament scripture in high regard. He knew that the Holy Spirit spoke by God's inspired Word.

Read **Hebrews 4:12, 2 Timothy 3:16, 2 Peter 1:20-21,** and **Psalm 19:7-10.**

5. Choose one or two facts about God's Word that you feel you could use to explain to someone how you feel about the Bible. Use them in a paragraph you could include in a letter to a friend.

____

____

____

____

6. The writer of Hebrews also knew that just as the Holy Spirit spoke to the people of God in the Old Testament, so He would speak to the readers to whom he was writing. What word in Hebrews 3:7 speaks of the relevance of God's Word?

____

Prayerfully read **Hebrews 3:7-11** again.

7. Underline words and phrases that speak directly to your mind and emotions, then paraphrase verse 7 into your own words.

____

____

____

____

I LISTEN (Journaling Suggestion)

Psalm 95 was well known to the Jews and was used as an invitation to worship in the temple and synagogue services. It's our invitation to worship too.

Worship has a way of keeping our hearts soft and this psalm is a call to do just that. Complete the following outline:

A. Come to sing for joy
   V. 1

B. Come to bow in worship
   V.
C. Come to hear His Voice
   V.

Explore these various aspects of worship as you have experienced them. How does this psalm add richness and meaning?

WE TALK TOGETHER (Prayer Suggestion)

List the various ways David sees God in Psalm 95. Use the name that speaks most directly to your heart as you talk to Him, e.g., "Lord, you are my Shepherd. . ."

❦ DAY 2 ❦

GOD SPEAKS

A LESSON FROM HISTORY

Read **Hebrews 3:7-19**.

1. Nobody wants others, particularly the ones they love, to make the same mistakes they did. Has someone ever told you a story from the past in hopes that you'd benefit in the present? What did he want you to learn?

   ____

   ____

   How did you respond?

   ____

   ____

As God speaks to His people, He calls to mind two incidents involving their ancesters in their forty years in the desert.

The first test is in the early part of their journey.

Read **Exodus 17:1-7.**

2. What were some of the indications that the people's hearts had become hardened?

The second test came when the Israelites camped at Kadesh-barnea. There God instructed them to send spies into the Promised Land to determine the country's strengths and weaknesses.

Read **Numbers 13:25-14:4.**

3. How did the Israelites respond to the spies' report?

4. How did God respond to the people's unbelief (Num. 14:20-23)?

5. What does the Israelites' response teach you about God?

6. What does it teach you about the dangers of a hard heart?

7. Rebellion is one symptom of a hard heart. What are other things that come out of a hardened heart?

____

____

I LISTEN

Today is a word that indicates now. Consider the following quotation from William Barclay:

> We speak easily about "tomorrow" but for us tomorrow may never come. All that we have is today. Someone has said: "We should live each day as it were a lifetime." God's offer must be accepted today; the trust and the obedience must be given today—for we cannot be sure that there will be a tomorrow for us.[1]

What do you feel that God would have you do "today"? What effect might your action have on your tomorrows? What difference might it make in eternity?

WE TALK TOGETHER

"Lord, the word *today* means while life lasts. Before this day closes I want to . . ."

❦ DAY 3 ❦

GOD SPEAKS

AN ANGRY GOD

Read **Hebrews 3:7-12.**

1. What is the difference between anger and wrath? Can we experience wrath and still be righteous?

____

____

1. William Barclay, *The Letter to the Hebrews*, rev. ed., The Daily Study Bible Series (Philadelphia, PA: Westminster Press, 1976), p. 34.

Psalm 95 brings together the two incidents in the wilderness we studied yesterday. Both incidents show how the Israelites consistently provoked God to anger. The word translated "angry" in Hebrews 3:10 is different from the "wrath" in verse 11, which speaks more directly to the strong opposition of God's holy nature to all that is evil. *The Amplified Bible* gives us insight. Keep in mind that God is speaking in verses 10-11.

> And so I was provoked (displeased and sorely grieved) with that generation, and said, They always err and are led astray in their hearts, and they have not perceived or recognized My ways and become progressively better and more experimentally intimately acquainted with them. Accordingly I swore in My wrath and indignation. They shall not enter into My rest (Heb. 3:10-11 TAB).

2. Compare this translation with that in the NIV. What additional understanding do you gain?

____

____

God is so concerned that His redeemed children will lose out on His peace and the rest of His presence by forsaking Him that He gives this warning in verse 12:

> [Therefore beware,] brethren; take care lest there be in any one of you a wicked, unbelieving heart—which refuses to cleave to, trust in and rely on Him—leading you to turn away and desert or stand aloof from the living God (Heb. 3:12 TAB).

3. How can this warning make a difference in the way you live your life—TODAY?

____

____

Called to Maturity

We are so conditioned to rationalize sin that it almost seems a good thing to do. We can even begin to expect it of God. "You thought that I was altogether like yourself" (Ps. 50:21).

Read **Romans 1:18, 3:23, 6:23.**

4. Is it difficult for you to see God as both a God of love and a God of wrath? Why or why not?

____

____

5. How would you rate your reaction to sin as compared to your Lord's reaction?

____

6. Perfect love and perfect holiness are displayed for us at Calvary. Draw a cross. On one of the arms write *love,* on the other *holiness.* Underneath write Romans 8:1-2.

The Bible is clear—God feels passionately about human sin. He knows that it has power to maim and destroy us, spiritually, emotionally, and physically.

7. How is God described in **Hebrews 12:29**?

___

In **Isaiah 66:12-16**?

___

We, as God's redeemed children, dwell within the consuming fire of God's presence. He is our protection.

I LISTEN

Rest is a concept indicating Israel's possession of a place *with* God (see Psalm 96:10), a place of security. Do you have a place like that? Describe it in your journal.

WE TALK TOGETHER

An old hymn reminds us: "A wall of fire about me, I've nothing now to fear. . . ." How might this challenge you to pray for those in your own family? Those you care about but who don't yet know Christ as their Savior, Lord or Protector?

❦ DAY 4 ❦

GOD SPEAKS

ENCOURAGING ONE ANOTHER

Read **Hebrews 3:12-15.**

1. Who has encouraged you most in your Christian life? What did they say? What did they do? If you could describe in one word how they felt about you, what would you say?

___

____

____

2. The writer of Hebrews has a tender concern for his readers. You might say he has a shepherd's heart—some have called Hebrews 3:12 the summary of pastoral exhortation. What word in verse 12 does he use to link his exhortation to Psalm 95?

____

How does he address his readers in this verse?

____

What do verses 12 and 13 tell you about the writer's concern for individuals believers?

____

____

____

How would you describe the heart of his exhortation?

____

____

3. Complete this sentence: "You cannot turn your back on Jesus Christ and not fall away from ______________________________

____."

This pastor writer places a high priority on encouragement among the people of God (Heb. 3:13; 10:25). He knows encouragement builds believers into a strong body.

4. Look up *encourage*, *encouraged*, *encouragement,* and *encouraging* in your concordance. Read several of the references in the New Testament. Which verses give you insight in how you might encourage other believers? Be ready to share several with your group.

___

5. Compare 3:14 with 3:6. How is the confidence and hope we are to hold on to in verse 6 identified in verse 14?

___

___

John Albert Bengel says, "A Christian, so long as he is not made perfect, considers himself as beginner."

6. How does this quotation encourage you?

___

Read **Hebrews 3:15.**

7. What familiar statement is the writer once again quoting?

___

What significance do these words from the Holy Spirit hold for you today?

___

___

How might you be able to use them to encourage another believer?

___

___

I LISTEN

God expects those who live by faith to give Him their undivided attention. You have just done that. Explain in your journal how He encouraged you personally—today. You might also want to write a note of encouragement to someone who has recently encouraged you. Mail it—today.

WE TALK TOGETHER

Pray for that one you feel God is encouraging you to encourage today.

❦ DAY 5 ❦

GOD SPEAKS

THE REST OF BELIEF

Read **Hebrews 3:16-19**.

1. Look up *rest* in the dictionary. Pick out words or phrases that are most inviting to you.

 ____

 ____

2. The writer uses the word *rest* for the first time in Hebrews 3:11. It's a word that we've heard often in this chapter. In fact the writer uses it _______ times in chapters 3 and 4.

The writer makes it clear that unbelief ends in death by using a series of rhetorical questions in vs. 15-18.

3. Which question hits you the hardest? Why?

 ____

 ____

 ____

4. What do you learn about the results of unbelief?

____

____

This chapter closes on a down note (v.19). For the other side of the story we need to take a quick look at Hebrews 4:3, "For we who have believed do enter that rest. . . ."

Rest is not only used for the promised heritage of Canaan but is also *rest* in a spiritual sense. There is a rest for those who continue on in their faith.

Read about the rest Jesus talked about in **Matthew 11:28-30.**

5. How does this rest make you feel?

____

____

Challenge activity: Rest and peace go together. Read the following scriptures that show both God and Jesus as our peace: Isaiah 9:6, Micah 5:4-5, Psalm 23:1-2, Ephesians 2:14-15, 1 Thessalonians 5:23, 2 Thessalonians 3:16.

Thought to mediate on: Jesus is not giving us an attribute in John 14:27. He's giving us Himself.

I LISTEN

Take Matthew 11: 28-30 into your day by writing your answers to the following questions in your journal. Since Jesus is inviting me to rest, what's keeping me from resting? Why am I gripping my burdens so tightly? Why am I so preoccupied with them, instead of Him? How can I experience the truth of being yoked with Him? What does being yoked with Him mean?

WE TALK TOGETHER

Write a prayer that personalizes what you're feeling and learning about rest.

Called to Maturity

WALKING ALONG TOGETHER

My first glimpse of Jesus Christ was one of rest and refreshment. Even now I can picture the two of us together. Me, a blonde five-year-old in a pink dress—Jesus, the tender Shepherd in a homespun brown robe. We sit together under the apple tree, talking together, enjoying each other's presence. There's even a big red apple on my lap.

The picture changes.

I'm older now—probably eight or nine. My two brothers and I are working at a table in the front yard. It's late summer and bees buzz around us. They try to land on our bare arms.

At our feet brown gunny sacks overflow with unhusked corn. In front of us are piles of golden corn ears.

My uncertain fingers grapple with husks and silk as my brothers cut and scrape the corn off the husks. Some of the canning jars covering the end of the table are empty but not for long. We take turns scooping the corn into the jars. After awhile I put several filled jars on a cookie sheet and, carefully balancing them, carry them into the house.

A blast of heat hits me as I enter the kitchen. The galvanized boiler on the back of the blackened kitchen range bubbles and smacks. Flames leap from the stove as Mother lifts the lid and shoves in more wood. Sweat drips off her forehead, stray hairs straggle from the bun at the back of her head.

Mother's Song

All of a sudden Mother bursts into song—"Oh, it's hard to be a Christian. Oh, it's hard to be a Christian. Oh, it's hard to be a Christian day by day."

I stare at her. *Well if it's so hard to be a Christian, why bother?*

As a grown up, I've often looked back at that memory. *Oh, Mother, I understand now what you meant. Sometimes it is hard to be a Christian, to keep perserving, to keep on when everything in us just wants to curl up and quit.*

Lord, I'd rather have the quiet rest—that place of intimacy and love I experienced underneath the apple tree. I'd rather sit tight in the circle of your arms and hear your voice whispering, "I will give you rest." And you do give it. Except the other times are there, too.

I know now that if I'm to grow in spiritual maturity there's a place for both—the rest of belief and trust, the labor of plain hard work. If

I'm to develop a spiritually balanced life I'm going to have to experience both. I only wish I knew how to put the two together.

Paul's Struggles

I have a feeling that Paul struggled in this area, too. I know he writes in 2 Timothy 4:10, "And for this we labor and strive (NIV)."

When I study the Greek word translated *labor*, I discover it means to work until one is weary. We even get our English word *agonize* from "strive," which means "to struggle."

In Colossians Paul writes, "I labor, struggling with all his energy, which so powerfully works in me" (Col. 1:29 NIV).

A light goes on inside my brain. Paul is laboring, but he's struggling in accord with the Spirit's power. Because He's in partnership with the Spirit of God, there's a rest.

Lord, I have to be honest. I've never really understood the "rest" of Hebrews. It's something I've struggled to comprehend. And then when it seems like I catch a tiny glimpse of it, it moves just a little further away.

I return now to Hebrews 3. Verse 14 in the NASB jumps out at me: "For we have become partakers of Christ, if we hold fast the beginning of our assurance firm until the end."

Holding Fast

My part is to "hold fast" and in Hebrews 4:14, I hear it again, "Seeing then that we have a great High Priest who has passed through the heavens, Jesus the Son of God, let us hold fast our confession."

And when I can't hang on any longer, I can cry out. He'll come running to me then. In His right hand is power and strength and mercy and grace.

Lord, the assurance that I'm a partaker in Jesus Christ means I can rest. And labor and strive and agonize and rest some more. You at my side means I can work toward a holy balance.

Lord, I'm tired tonight. But because You're the Living God who does more than your part, I can let go. I can rest.

I pick up the phone. I want to share with Mother what I'm learning. I hear the ring at the other end—her quiet "hell-o."

Conversation with My Mother

Words burst from me. "Mother, do you remember how you sang

that it was hard to be a Christian? You were canning corn and we didn't have electricity and the kitchen was so hot.

"Mother, I didn't understand what you meant then, but I do now. I love you for the way you poured out the agony of your weariness to God—You turned to Him when you could have so easily have turned the other way—.

"Yes, Mother. I know. But because you turned to Jesus, I can look at your life today. You'll be eighty-five your next birthday and you're still standing firm. Jesus shines out of your eyes."

I cradle the phone closer. Tears prickle my eyes. "Yes, I know it's hard to be a Christian. What's that? You want me to beware of a hard heart? You're warning me to not drift away from what I've been taught?

"But, Mother, I don't have to turn away. You taught me that. And so has the writer of Hebrews. Jesus is there for me. When I turn to Him, His arms are open wide.

"Because they are, I can rest. . . ."

I smile as I hang up the phone. I open my journal, begin to write. *I called Mother tonight. Something she said I don't want to forget. "Jesus doesn't think we're lazy when we put aside work to sit at His feet."*

Lord, thank you for my Mother. . . .

7

• • •

A Place of Rest

Hebrews 4:1-13

❦ DAY 1 ❦

GOD SPEAKS

A BACKWARD LOOK

Read **Hebrews 3:6-4:11**.

1. Finish these sentences:
   The kind of rest that most appeals to me right now is . . .
   For me rest means . . .
   a. taking a nap after lunch
   b. sunbathing at the beach
   c. reading a mystery novel until 2 a.m.
   d. going home to mother

2. The admonition to enter God's rest grows out of our history lesson from last week. For the Israelites, rest was a place called

the ______________________. What was it that kept them from entering it?

____

Read **Hebrews 3:16-19**.

3. What kind of a picture is painted for us in these verses?

____

____

4. Why do you think the writer of Hebrews is giving us such a tragic picture?

____

____

In Exodus 17:1-7 the Israelites stood at a crossroad. They stood at still another in Numbers 13:25-14:4. Both times they had a choice—they could either enter God's rest or harden their hearts.

5. Look at the diagram below. What two choices did the Israelites make in both accounts?

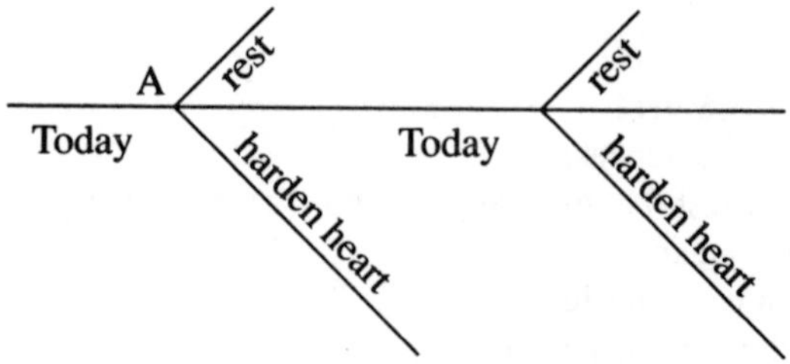

Picture yourself standing at point A. What directions would you give the Israelites?

Draw a warning sign you could display at these crucial points in history.

6. Look back at your own past, that time when you took a wrong turn. Knowing what you know today, how would you have chosen differently?

   Did you notice the repeated "Today" on the diagram? What does this tell you about the choices you make on a daily basis?

I LISTEN (Journaling Suggestion)

Are you at a crossroads right now? Evaluate it in the light of today's study. Which direction presents the greater opportunity to trust God?

WE TALK TOGETHER

God's special place of rest is always the place closest to His heart. Ask Him to give you the courage to take His way even though it may appear to be leading into a valley of shadow.

❦ DAY 2 ❦

GOD SPEAKS

OBSERVING THE TEXT

Read **Hebrews 4:1-11.**

1. Have you ever failed to communicate something because you used a word that didn't mean the same thing to the person you were talking to? Explain.

____

____

____

____

This chapter is quite possibly the most complicated in the entire book of Hebrews. It is probably best to go for the heart of its message rather than struggle with too many details which, in this chapter, have a tendency to confuse.

2. Read the entire passage. Personalize the grand sweep of what you read into a sentence or two. It may help you to begin your sentence something like this: God's grand plan was . . .

____

____

____

One of the problems in this chapter is that the writer is using rest in three different ways.

a. Rest as God's peace

b. Rest as a place—the Promised Land

c. The rest of completing a task—the creation rest God experienced after creating the world

3. Now go through the chapter and underline each "rest" as you try to determine the writer's meaning of each one. Designate what you think it means by using the following abbreviations: P - Peace; P.L. - Promised Land; C.R. - Creation Rest. We'll learn more about each of these this week

Just as God rested from the work of creation, those who believe God's Word stop trying to gain salvation by their works. Instead they rest in the finished work of Jesus Christ on the cross.

Read **Ephesians 2:8-10.**

4. How does it make you feel to know that none of your own efforts can save you? That salvation is God's free gift to those who believe?

____

____

____

I LISTEN

Look for a chorus or hymn that talks about "rest." Write some of the words of the one you choose into your journal.

WE TALK TOGETHER

Sing the song you chose to your Lord. Don't be afraid to add your own verses. Creating something new is one way we enter God's rest.

❦ DAY 3 ❦

GOD SPEAKS

A SHELTERED PLACE OF PEACE

Read **Hebrews 4:1-11.**

1. Name one or two places you most want to go when you're troubled or under a lot of pressure.

Reread **Hebrews 4:1-11.**

2. This time underline every place that talks about entering God's rest. How many "enters" did you find?

3. God's promise of rest was more than just entering the Promised Land. Which verses in chapters 3 and 4 emphasize that truth?

4. The way *rest* is used in Hebrews 4 speaks of entering a room or a space. What special places does God provide for us by giving us Himself (Ps. 31:2-3, 91:4; Prov. 18:10)?

Placing your complete trust in your God is a first step toward entering His rest. Just as those who entered the physical rest in Canaan had to believe in God's promise, so must we believe that salvation rest is entered only by faith in Jesus Christ.

5. How does it make you feel to realize that the rest God calls you to enter (vv. 9-11) is not your rest at all but His, and that He's inviting you to share it with Him?

____

I LISTEN

Draw a winged creature: eagle or a bird of your choice. Underneath your drawing write Psalm 91:4, "Under His wings you shall take refuge." Claim it for your own by writing your name for *you*, Jesus for *refuge*.

WE TALK TOGETHER

In Psalm 31:1-4, David calls God his rock of refuge and his fortress of defense. Use one or both of these names as you call upon Him now.

❦ DAY 4 ❦

GOD SPEAKS

THE SABBATH-REST

Read **Hebrews 4:8-11.**

1. How do you feel when you've completed a task, particularly one in which you exercised a lot of creativity?

____

We've seen from Psalm 95 that the rest God gave His people when they entered Canaan wasn't the complete picture of the rest He had in mind.

Read **Hebrews 4:3-4, 8-10**. Gain even more insight by reading the following: **Genesis 2:2; Exodus 20:11, 31:16-17**.

2. How is the Sabbath a picture of rest?

____

Called to Maturity

The Sabbath was more than a day of rest from work. It was a spiritual rest involving an awareness of being in the presence of God with His people. A day to worship and praise (Ps. 100).

3. Describe the rest you've experienced as you've worshiped with other believers.

____

____

4. Spiritual rest is for now but it is also for later. When we die we enter a rest that is eternal (Rev. 14:13). Who are these blessed dead?

____

Read **Revelation 21:4** for a more complete picture of this heavenly rest.

5. What do you observe?

____

____

I LISTEN

Read **Psalm 95:6-7**. How does it make you feel to be one of the Lord's sheep experiencing His care and protection while you are here on earth? Read **Revelation 7:15-17**. Praise Him for that heavenly scene where all who love the Lamb, who is also the Shepherd, will gather to worship.

WE TALK TOGETHER

Do you know someone who has refused to believe in Jesus Christ? Someone who, if they continue in the way they're now headed, will not be among the throng worshipping God in heaven? Pray for that one today.

❦ DAY 5 ❦

GOD SPEAKS

THE WORD OF GOD

Read **Hebrews 4:12-13.**

1. Have you ever experienced rest as you've read God's Word? Why do you think this was so? Have you ever read God's Word and experienced unrest? In light of Hebrews 4:13, why might this be?

____

____

____

____

The verses in today's study almost seem to interrupt the flow of God's rest. But not really. Now that we understand more about the importance of resting we need a little help in how to apply that rest. God's Word gives us that help.

2. We find three characteristics of the Word of God in the first part of verse 12:

a. It is L ______________________________

b. It is P ______________________________

c. It is S ______________________________

We find two of its abilities in the latter part of the verse.

a. It has the ability to P ______________________________

b. It has the ability to D ______________________________

Called to Maturity

3. Underline the words that speak of how God exposes the secret places inside our hearts in verse 13. What does this tell you about God?

____

____

____

Words were especially important to the Jew. William Barclay writes about it in *The Letter to the Hebrews:*

> The Jews always had a special idea about words. Once a word was spoken, it had an independent existence. It was not only a sound with a certain meaning; it was a power which went forth and did things. Isaiah heard God say that the word which went out of his mouth would never be ineffective; it would always do that which God designed it to do.[1]

Read **Isaiah 55:11.**

4. Compare the way you regard your Bible, God's holy Word, to the way Isaiah and the writer of Hebrews felt about it.

____

____

____

____

The original readers stood shoulder to shoulder with other believers, listening to Hebrews being read. They heard God's warning of what would happen if they disregarded His invitation to enter His rest.

---

1. William Barclay, *The Letter to the Hebrews*, rev. ed., The Daily Study Bible Series (Philadelphia, PA: Westminster Press, 1976), pp. 38-39.

5. How do you think they felt when they heard the powerful description of God's Word in Hebrews 4:12-13? Remember, they're experiencing persecution. They're tired, ready to give up. How could these particular verses encourage them?

____

____

____

____

Challenge activity: God's Word is living and powerful, sharper than any two-edged sword. It discerns the thoughts and intents of the heart. One of the ways you can take these words into your mind and heart is by memorizing Hebrews 4:12-13. Write the verses on a filecard. Read them out loud slowly, phrase by phrase. Put the card in your pocket or in a prominent place you go often. Read and reread throughout the day. Meditate on what these verses mean. Do this until you can quote the verses from memory.

I LISTEN

Whenever women take God's Word seriously, things begin to happen. What do you want God's Word to do for you today?

WE TALK TOGETHER

American Christians probably take their Bibles more for granted than any other people in the world. Take time to thank God for His Word today.

WALKING ALONG TOGETHER

"You live in a shack. Your house is a chicken coop."

Niner, niner, niner. Sticks and stones may break my bones but words will never hurt me.

"Those old newspapers stuffed in your windowsills look awful. I can see them from the road."

Run, run, run. Sticks and stones may break my bones but words will never hurt me.

Except it isn't true. Words do have power to hurt. The agony of being rejected by my jeering classmates sears my heart.

Run. Run. Run. *Sticks and stones may break my bones . . .* Climb. Climb. Climb. *But words will never hurt me.* Higher and higher—into the very heart of the great cherry tree. The branches on top are shaped like airplane wings. Only instead of being straight across, they gently curve. My tree cradles me as I tuck myself into its arms.

The careless words of the kids on the school bus can't follow me up here. No one can. At least no one ever did. That cherry tree was my refuge, my safe place.

I think about that tree in the spring when I smell cherry blossoms and hear bees buzz. Sometimes the memory has a bittersweet feel—Daddy chopped down the tree the summer he thought rot had spread into the center of the trunk. After that I climbed the prune tree in the orchard or the vine maple at the top of the hill.

Another Safe Place

Now that I'm grown I have another safe place. Only my place isn't really a place at all. It's a Person—the Lord Jesus Christ. He's with me all the time. When I'm working at the computer or filing papers away for safe keeping. When I'm preparing a stew or hugging a grandchild.

Sometimes, though, I see His heart more clearly when we're alone together. Like today. I need to take a walk. I need to talk and talk.

I pick up my Bible and journal and slip out of the house. *Lord, there's a relationship that's bugging me. I can't seem to let go of it.*

The hurt inside me wells into a stream. I know now why I've been avoiding even thinking about my friend. The loss I feel stabs my heart. I'm being cut into ribbons. . .

Lord, I don't understand. You've given me such a burden for her restoration. And I've been a part of it. I know I have. But now she's running from me. She says she can't bear to see my face. Or hear my voice.

And it's not even my fault. I didn't do anything. It's just that I represent her failure, her hurt.

Lord, I've prayed. And agonized. I've even fasted for her . . . for the ministry she once had, the ministry I've been given faith to believe will be restored.

But now she's cut me off. I don't know how to handle it.

I leave the road and enter a thicket of hazelnut and wild plum. The cedar tree with the curved trunk just made for sitting invites me inside. The creek is almost still—a water skipper makes a pattern on the surface of the water.

Alone with the Lord

I sit down and lean back against the cedar tree. Tears slip down my cheeks as I close my eyes. There's no one to see—only my Lord.

My morning study in the book of Hebrews nudges me. The writer of Hebrews reminded me that God's Word scrutinizes a woman's desires—that emotional part governed by her feelings, her instincts and passions. He reminded me that His Word examines her motives—her mind. It was as if He said, "Your emotions and mind must be submitted to My scrutiny. Eva, I want you to look into My eyes."

But I don't want to open my eyes. I want to hide in the safety of the darkness. I don't even want Jesus, my best friend, to see my hurt. Maybe if I just pretend it doesn't matter, the pain will go away.

But I can't go on like this. His Spirit compels me to open His Word. I turn to Hebrews 4.

A verse jumps out at me. "Today, if you will hear My voice, do not harden your hearts."

I've been hardening my heart, haven't I, Lord? Not wanting to face the hurt I feel has made me close off a part of who I am from You.

A whisper of peace settles around me. "For anyone who enters my rest also rests from her own work, just as I did from mine."

Lord, there's nothing I can do or say to help my friend. Is that what you're saying? That all I can do right now is rest from my work and trust in Yours?

Relinquishing My Friend

My hand opens. She's in my palm. I lift my hand to Him. In the best way I know how, I give her to my Lord.

I read. "Seeing then that we have a great High Priest who has passed through the heavens, Jesus the Son of God, let us hold fast our confession."

Another verse niggles in my mind. *Lord, is it Your Spirit?*

I turn the pages. Romans 8:32: "How shall He not also freely give us all things?" "Christ, who died and furthermore is also risen, who is even at the right hand of God who also makes intercession for us" (v. 34).

At the Father's Right Hand

Yes, it fits. I've seen Jesus at the Father's right hand more than once since I've started this study in Hebrews. It's a picture of His sovereignty. His glory. His majesty.

"Let us therefore come boldly to the throne of grace, that we may obtain mercy and find grace to help us in time of need" (Heb. 4:16).

I remember my blossom-scented childhood refuge in the cherry tree. I have so much more now. I have Him. I have His Word. His presence is real.

I can write in my journal now.

Lord, I'm in your throne room. It's a place of rest. A place of peace. And yes, I'll be honest. It's a place of pain, too. But Lord You're greater than my hurt. You've promised me grace and mercy in my time of need.

I look up, up into His face—into His eyes. They smile at me.

"Restore us, O Lord God of hosts;
Cause Your face to shine,
And we shall be saved" (Ps. 80:19).

It's my prayer for me and my friend.

8

Our High Priest at the Throne of Grace

Hebrews 4:14-16

DAY 1

GOD SPEAKS

PROFESSING OUR FAITH

Read **Hebrews 4:14-16.**

1. If someone asked you to tell one particular thing about Jesus Christ that has impacted you during this study, what would you say?

Called to Maturity

2. What are the two names in verse 14 that describe Jesus? What is their significance?

____

____

____

In this paragraph the writer concludes his comparison of Christ and Moses. Now he presents the very heart of God—Jesus is the great High Priest!

The first century Jews were able to talk about animals, blood, and high priests in the same way people today talk about sports—baseball—football— basketball. But the Old Testament sacrificial system isn't that easy for us to understand.

3. Quickly jot down one or two facts about the Old Testament High Priest that you already know.

____

____

The writer lists three qualifications for a priest in Hebrews 5:1-4.

a. He must represent God (v. 1-2)
b. He must offer sacrifices for sin (v. 3)
c. He must be called (appointed) by God. (v. 4)

4. How did Jesus meet these qualifications?

____

____

____

____

Our High Priest at the Throne of Grace

The Jewish High Priest entered the inner sanctuary of the temple once a year and stood for a short time in God's presence.

Read **Hebrews 1:3, 4:14, 7:26-27, 9:24.**

5. Finish the following sentence: By contrast, Jesus . . .

____

____

____

6. What is the faith you profess (Heb. 4:14)?

____

Read **Romans 10:10.**

7. How have these verses been a reality in your life?

____

____

____

____

I LISTEN

Think through your own personal testimony of how you came to know Christ and what He means to you now. You will have an opportunity to share your testimony with the group when you meet together for your last study in this book.

WE TALK TOGETHER

The term *great* in Hebrews 4:14 is also found in Hebrews 10:21 in some versions. (Jesus is also called the great Shepherd of the sheep in Hebrews 13:20.) This adjective tells us Jesus is superior to any earthly high priest or shepherd. Why not tell Him how great you think He is today?

❦ DAY 2 ❦

GOD SPEAKS

A HIGH PRIEST WHO SYMPATHIZES

Read **Hebrews 4:15**.

1. When you say someone has a sympathetic heart, what do you mean?

___

___

___

2. Underline the double negative in v. 15. State the positive idea.

___

___

The Greek word for *sympathize* here is the same word translated "compassion" or "pity" and was used nine times in the Gospels to describe Jesus. The intensity of emotion Jesus felt for people compelled Him to do something.

3. Write down the action Jesus took in each of the following examples:

   a. **Matthew 14:14-19** ___

   b. **Matthew 20:29-34** ___

   c. **Mark 1:40-45** ___

   d. **Luke 7:11-15** ___

4. How does it make you feel to realize that Jesus is just as emotionally involved with you when you are tempted as He was with those He helped when He was here on earth?

Read **Matthew 4:1-11** and **27:42-44.**

5. In what ways were the results of Jesus' temptation different from yours?

Jesus was tempted as we are—and far beyond. Only He who doesn't yield knows temptation in its full force.

I LISTEN

Read **1 Corinthians 10:13, Hebrews 2:18, 4:16 and 13:6**. What specific help does God promise to you? What are you to do in order to receive it?

Writing down God's Part and My Part for each reference will help you clarify God's message for you.

	God's Part	My Part
1 Corinthians 10:13:		
Hebrews 2:18:		
Hebrews 4:14-16:		
Hebrews 13:6:		

WE TALK TOGETHER

Jesus is your powerful advocate and helper. Talk to Him today about a specific temptation that you often struggle with.

❦ DAY 3 ❦

GOD SPEAKS

THE GLORY OF GRACE AND MERCY

Read **Hebrews 4:16.**

1. Name one person that you feel you could go to with a problem you have. What is there about that person that makes them approachable?

____

____

Reread **Hebrews 4:16.**

2. Draw a line from the "let us" in verse 14 to the "let us" in 16. What two things are we invited to do in these two verses?

____

____

3. What word does the writer use to include himself in God's invitation to come to the throne of grace?

____

4. How does this word show that the mediation of earthly priests is no longer necessary? Also read **Hebrews 7:25 and 9:24.**

____

____

Our High Priest at the Throne of Grace

"The throne of grace" is a heavenly symbol—an earthly description of prayer—the place where we meet the Son of God who is the King (Heb. 1:2-4).

We are invited to come confidently to the King's throne. Jesus Himself stands there at the Father's right hand. He holds out His golden scepter saying, "Come."

5. What is He willing to give you?

____

6. Some have interpreted *mercy* and *grace* as synonyms. However, there is a difference. How have people tried to explain these words to you?

____

____

____

Scholars have tried to define the difference between grace and mercy. Consider the following quotations:

> We draw near to that throne to obtain mercy, for we are conscious of our sin; we draw near to receive grace, for we confess our weakness.[1]

> Mercy is to be "taken" as it is extended to man in his weakness; grace is to be "sought" by man according to his necessity.[2]

> We need mercy because we have failed so often, and we need grace because service awaits us in which we need God's help.[3]

---

1. Charles R. Erdman, *The Epistle to the Hebrews* (Philadelphia, PA: The Westminster Press, 1934), p. 54.
2. Westcott, *Hebrews*, p. 109.
3. Leon Morris, *Expositor's Bible Commentary* (Grand Rapids, MI: The Zondervan Corporation, 1981), Vol. 12, p. 46.

Called to Maturity

7. Put a star by the quotation that gives you the most understanding.

8. The needs we have at the moment can be wide ranged: lack of communication in a marriage, financial stress, worry over a friend, a son, or daughter, a physical, or spiritual need. According to Hebrews 4:14-16 how might Jesus empathize with your particular need?

____

____

How might prayer be a part of the solution?

____

____

I LISTEN

Describe a significant memory of what God did for you when you couldn't do anything for yourself. You might entitle it, "A Song of Grace."

WE TALK TOGETHER

What pressing need do you have today? God is inviting you to bring it to His throne.

❦ DAY 4 ❦

GOD SPEAKS

A BACKWARD LOOK

Read **Hebrews 1 and 2 with 4:16.**

1. Recall a time in your life when you felt you needed to evaluate what's gone on before. What did you learn from your backward look?

Although chapter 4 closes with the throne of grace, it is really the beginning. Jesus as the great High Priest is the heart of this epistle.

Earlier we saw Jesus as superior to the prophets and to the angels. We saw Him as greater than Moses.

In 4:14 we're introduced to Him as the great High Priest, who is greater than any earthly priest. In 4:16 we see Him in heaven at the throne of grace.

2. Put together observations from Hebrews 4:14-16 and Hebrews 1:1-4. Finish the following thought: Jesus didn't go to heaven to retire. He went there to . . .

3. Does the description of Jesus Christ in Hebrews 1:1-4 mean more to you now than when you first studied it? In what way?

Read **Hebrews 1:5-14**.

4. How does the description of God's throne in Hebrews 1:8-9 add to your understanding of the throne of grace in 4:16?

Called to Maturity

Read **Hebrews 2:1-4.**

5. How has Jesus as the great High Priest heightened your appreciation of the great salvation mentioned in these verses?

____

____

6. What evidences of this great salvation have you been able to see working in your life since you first studied this warning?

____

____

____

Read **Hebrews 2:5-18.**

7. Pick out several verses that emphasize Jesus' sacrifice on Calvary.

____

____

____

I LISTEN

Read **Leviticus 16:20-22 and 17:11**. The blood of these Old Testament sacrifices pointed to Jesus, the Lamb of God. His blood has "once for all" obtained for us "eternal redemption" (Heb. 9:12) for "without shedding of blood there is no remission" (Heb. 9:22)

Find a chorus or hymn that proclaims the blood of Jesus Christ. Try paraphrasing the words to make them your own. Perhaps you will want to write your own praise words about the blood of Jesus and put them to music.

WE TALK TOGETHER

Redemption is a powerful word. Address your prayer today to your Powerful Redeemer.

❦ DAY 5 ❦

GOD SPEAKS

REMAINING FAITHFUL

Read **Hebrews 3 and 4**.

1. Whenever we write someone a letter we do so with a specific purpose in mind. Think about the last letter you wrote. Who did you write to? What was your purpose in writing?

____

____

The writer of Hebrews has a pastor's heart. His purpose in writing is to encourage the Hebrews to remain faithful to God and His Word. To continue to grow in spiritual maturity.

2. Look back to where you were eight weeks ago. What new beginnings of spiritual growth do you see?

____

____

Sometimes others can see things in us that we can't see for ourselves. You might want to ask a trusted friend if she has observed any measurable spiritual growth in you. Ask her to pray for you in this area.

3. In chapters 3 and 4 we learned how important it was to rest—how important it was to "labor" to enter that rest. What truth about His rest has made the most impact on you?

____

____

Called to Maturity

How have you applied it in your life this week?

____

____

____

God's Word helps us apply the rest of God to our lives. Not only does it show us what's going on deep inside our hearts—The writer's description of the Word in Hebrews 4:12-13 is powerful.

4. What part of this description has been most meaningful to you this week?

____

____

____

Reread **the first four chapters of Hebrews.**

5. Write down every name used for God.

____

____

Challenge activity: Make an acrostic of the Name that means the most to you right now.

I LISTEN

Chapter four ends at the throne of grace, a quiet reminder that God's Word and prayer are foundational for spiritual growth. What would you write in a letter to a fellow believer who wants to know why God's Word and prayer are so important?

WE TALK TOGETHER

Ask God to help you keep growing day by day. You need His strength to keep you faithfully persevering in His Word, in prayer, and in obedience.

WALKING ALONG TOGETHER

Grace. Even as a little girl I knew there was something special about that word. Whenever I heard anyone say it, I thought of mayflowers, miniature ferns, and tiny silver waterfalls tinkling against rocks.

Grace lost some of its allure when I heard someone describe grace as God's unmerited favor. God I knew, but I didn't know what unmerited meant, and as for favor—I wasn't anyone's favorite that I knew of.

Later someone showed me the grace acrostic:

God's
Riches
At
Christ's
Expense

I liked the way the letters lined up. And I liked the way the word sounded when I whispered it to the trilliums and mayflowers in the woods. What it actually meant remained a mystery.

My Friend, Geri

Years later, a grown woman with children of my own, I met Geri at a writer's conference. Geri was everything I could ever hope to be. In a way she resembled the grace I glimpsed as a small child—the elusive scent of lavender mayflowers. The silver sound of a waterfall in a forest glade.

Geri became my friend. We attended writer's conferences together, critiqued each other's manuscripts. When my daughter ran away, Geri prayed for her. When she came back to the Lord, she discipled her.

Then cancer.

Geri was lying on the couch the day I visited shortly after she'd heard the doctor's fearsome words. I took her hands in mine and held on tight. "Eva," she said, "I'd like to spend more time with you."

Her words were God's call to me. After that we met weekly for prayer and sharing from our personal quiet times with the Lord.

Geri was a drama professor, a librarian, a gifted writer. This gracious woman became my mentor—my best friend. We rejoiced together at her remission, we prayed when things got worse again.

Almost six years later Geri took to her bed. This time she didn't get up.

I visited her more often then. The day came when she could no longer read or write.

"Eva . . ." she whispered one morning.

I leaned close.

"I've known Jesus for a long time."

I waited.

The Meaning of Grace

"What does God's grace mean? Oh, I understand about unmerited favor and God's riches but what is grace really? Eva, I have to know."

The darkness and confusion in her eyes drove pain deep in my soul. How could I answer?

Suddenly I knew. "Geri, I think grace is just God doing for us what we can't do for ourselves."

She closed her eyes and I bowed my head. *Lord, meet Geri at her point of need. Please, do for her what I can't do. Give her the gift of grace—Your grace.*

I visited again a few days later. She smiled at me through her weakness.

"Your words—." Her struggle to express her heart almost broke mine. I held tight to her hand. "Eva, your words meant so much."

I was unprepared for the joy that suddenly flashed in her brown eyes, the strength in her voice. "Grace is simply God doing for me what I can't do for myself."

Before I left she said, "I'm experiencing His grace. His peace. He is enough."

God met Geri again at her point of need a few days later when He took her home to be with Him. He did for her what she couldn't do for herself.

I know now that God's grace is more than lavender mayflowers. It is faith and love and hope—forgiveness and gentleness—joy and peace all wrapped up together. Grace is what gives us strength to hang on and cling tight even when everything falls apart. Even when life ends.

It's been a year now since Geri went to heaven. I miss her. . . .

In the Midst of Busyness

Today I was so busy. Almost too busy—bulletins to print and run—letters to prepare. The friend who was going to come and pray with me never showed. And hard things are happening at home—Bud called twice.

Lord, I feel alone tonight. But I don't have to be alone. I can be with You at the throne of grace . . .

God's Word is part of that throne. I reach for my Bible, my journal— pull my concordance off the shelf. I want to discover more about His grace.

I scan the *grace* references, put tiny dots alongside the ones I want to look up. The first is Psalm 45:2, "Your lips have been anointed with grace (NIV)."

I know from my study in Hebrews that the psalmist is talking about my Lord Jesus Christ—the writer of Hebrews quoted from this psalm in chapter two.

My Amplified Bible is beside me. Psalm 45—I note the preface, *A song of loves.* I read the first verse: "My heart overflows with a goodly theme; I address my psalm to a king. My tongue is as the pen of a ready writer."

I know what it's like to have an overflowing heart, to have inside me a longing to address a song to the King . . . the Lord of life.

I begin to write. My song paraphrases Psalm 45.

A Song of Loves

Lord Jesus, you are excellent—superior—more glorious than any other. God Himself has anointed Your lips with His grace. He has blessed You forever!

Oh, Jesus, Mighty Warrior, Your Word is a sword that pierces my heart. It proclaims truth, humility, and righteousness.

It even fights for me for I am your daughter.

Lord Jesus, You stand at the throne of grace in heaven. You're there right now at the Father's right hand. You are fragrance, music—joy.

Lord, I'm here at your invitation.

As I come near, You hold out to me the scepter of Your forgiveness. You are both King and High Priest—my Mediator, Advocate, Intercessor. I bow before You.

I give you my loneliness. My pain . . .

Because I come, You give power and strength. You do for me what

Called to Maturity

I can't do for myself.
I worship You.

I close my notebook but my heart lingers in His presence.

God's grace empowered Geri to be faithful to the end, to grow in beauty even while physical weakness engulfed her. She is one of the princesses whose gown is interwoven with gold in Psalm 45.

The Endurance of Grace

I understand a little more now—the entire movement of the Christian life from beginning to end is grace. Grace comes from God to man. When we receive it, we're empowered to give to others. We become links in the chain of grace, a chain that goes on and on—the stronger coming to help the weaker, the weaker becoming stronger, helping another who's weaker . . .

Grace empowers us to endure to the end.

"Therefore, dear friends, since you already know this, be on your guard so that you may not be carried away by the error of lawless men and fall from your secure position. But grow in the grace and knowledge of our Lord and Savior Jesus Christ. To him be glory both now and forever! Amen. (2 Pet. 3:17-18 NIV).

"The grace of our Lord Jesus Christ be with you all. Amen" (Rev. 22:21).